John Harrold.

This book belongs to:

....

CONTENTS

STORIES BY IAN ROBINSON
ILLUSTRATED BY JOHN HARROLD
STORY COLOURING BY GINA HART

John Harrold

RUPERT

THE EXPRESS ANNUAL

John Harrold.

No 66

Published by Pedigree Books Limited
The Old Rectory, Matford Lane, Exeter, Devon, EX2 4PS
email: books@pedigreegroup.co.uk

£6.99
RU66

RUPERT and

*One summer morning, Rupert comes
Across one of his favourite chums...*

It is a fine summer's day and Rupert has gone for a walk across Nutwood common... "I wonder if I'll meet anyone?" he thinks. "Most of my friends are still away on holiday..." Just then, Rupert hears a far-off cry. He looks up and spots Ottoline Otter, coming from the direction of Nutwood Court. "Hello!" she smiles. "I was hoping there'd be someone here. Shall we go for a walk in the woods?" "Good idea!" nods Rupert. "We can try looking for birds."

the Coronation

*It's Ottoline - who thinks they should
Both go exploring in the wood...*

*"Let's go bird-spotting! Some are rare -
While others you see everywhere."*

"This is fun!" laughs Ottoline as the pals start to explore. "Let's see who can spot the rarest bird. Robins and finches are easy. It's tree-creepers and wrens that are harder to find." As the pair go quietly forward, Rupert suddenly hears a far-off sound... "Listen!" he whispers. "A woodpecker!" says Ottoline. "That really would be exciting! I wonder if we can get close enough to see it?" "Let's try!" smiles Rupert. "Follow me..."

*"A woodpecker!" gasps Rupert. "We
Might spot it, high up in a tree."*

7

RUPERT AND OTTOLINE GET LOST

The two pals follow the bird's trail -
"Hurrah!" calls Rupert. "There's its tail..."

The friends are lost. "We've come so far
I really don't know where we are!"

At last the two chums find a track.
"I think that this might lead us back..."

They reach a road. "Listen! I hear
The sound of hoof-beats drawing near."

Fascinated by the sound of the woodpecker, Rupert and Ottoline follow it deeper and deeper into the forest... "Up there!" calls Rupert triumphantly. "I saw a glimpse of green!" "You're right!" cries Ottoline. "Aren't they hard to spot! No wonder I've only ever heard woodpeckers before..." The chums have been so intent on following the bird, it is only as it flies off that they realise how far they have wandered from the path... "Which way now?" asks Ottoline. "I...I don't know!" admits Rupert.

To the pals' relief, they finally come to a narrow track leading through the forest. "Let's follow this and see where it goes," says Rupert. "Even if it's the wrong way, we should still reach a proper road..." Sure enough, the chums eventually come to an opening in the trees, where the path joins a winding trail... "Good!" says Rupert. "Now all we need to do is find out where it leads." "Listen!" says Ottoline. "I can hear the sound of hoof-beats. There must be somebody coming..."

RUPERT MEETS TWO HORSEMEN

The horsemen who appear both look
As though they're from a history book...

The rider kneels. "Can this be true?
My lady! Is it really you?"

"'Tis lucky that we rode this way -
We'll take you home without delay!"

"It won't take long. We'll soon be there!"
The horsemen reassure the pair.

Before the startled chums can move, they see two riders come galloping along the road towards them... "Look at their clothes!" gasps Ottoline. "They're like something from a history book!" Rupert is astonished too, but what follows amazes him even more... Stopping his horse abruptly, the leading rider dismounts and kneels respectfully at Ottoline's feet. "The Lady Ottoline!" he exclaims. "Without guards and retainers... Can this be true? How come you so far from home?"

"I...I got lost in the woods!" says Ottoline, still marvelling at the man's strange clothes and speech. "Rupert found a path but we still weren't sure which way to go..." "'Tis a lucky meeting!" the rider smiles. "On horseback the journey home is easy. Come, Princess. Your friend shall accompany us too. My fellow-huntsman will take him, while you ride with me..." In a matter of moments, the chums are travelling through the forest with their new companions, who urge the horses on...

RUPERT IS TAKEN TO A CASTLE

"We've left the forest!" Rupert blinks.
"This can't be the right way!" he thinks...

"A castle!" marvels Ottoline.
The chums both gasp at what they've seen.

"Amazing!" Rupert murmurs. "I'm
Quite sure we've travelled back in time..."

A stranger gasps in shocked surprise -
"P...Princess Ottoline!" he cries.

As the riders leave the forest, Rupert looks for familiar landmarks... "I don't see any!" he blinks. "Perhaps we're going the wrong way?" "Not far now!" calls the leading horseman. "You'll soon be safely home." Ottoline is amazed when she spots what lies at the end of the twisting trail. "A castle!" she gasps. "But this isn't Nutwood!" "No, Lady!" laughs her escort. "'Tis the stronghold of your ancestors. Nutwood is but one of their possessions. A hamlet on the far side of the forest..."

Marvelling at the stranger's words, Rupert and Ottoline find themselves riding through the castles main gates into a large courtyard... "Everybody's wearing old-fashioned clothes!" blinks Rupert. "We must have travelled back in time..." As the chums dismount a richly-robed figure with a gold chain around his neck comes hurrying out to see who's there... "P...Princess Ottoline!" he stammers. "What a surprise! Wherever have you been? I'd no idea you'd left the castle."

RUPERT IS NOT ALLOWED IN

"The Princess wandered miles from home –
Too far for her to safely roam..."

"I'm so relieved that you were found –
Thank goodness that you're safe and sound!"

As Rupert follows, two guards say
He's not allowed – and bar the way...

"For uninvited guests, like you,
Straw in the stables there will do!"

"We went bird-spotting," explains Ottoline. "And lost our way..." "I found them in the woods," adds the horseman. "Miles from the castle..." "Bless me!" blinks the other man. "Thank goodness you're back! As Court Chamberlain I'm responsible for your safety. A Princess can't just wander off! The future of the whole Kingdom depends on your well-being." Ottoline tries to tell the Chamberlain that he has made a mistake but he laughs and leads her to the main hall. "Come, Lady. Let us join the others..."

Rupert follows closely after Ottoline and the Chamberlain but, as he reaches the door, two stern sentries bar the way. "No commoners in the Great Hall!" one growls. "The Chamberlain and Princess Ottoline are dining in state. Strangers are permitted by invitation only!" Rupert looks so startled that the second guard takes pity on him and points towards the stables. "You can shelter there, if you like." he suggests. "The Groom won't mind and at least the straw will keep you warm."

RUPERT'S FRIEND HAS A FEAST

"It's so strange! I don't understand –
Like being in another land!"

As Rupert waits outside he hears
A banquet start, with songs and cheers...

"From out here I can see them all –
They're feasting in the castle hall!"

"At least Ottoline's having fun –
She seems to have fooled everyone!"

Rupert walks over to the stables and sits outside. "What shall I do?" he wonders. "There must be some mistake. They all seem to think that Ottoline's a Princess! Everyone's been making such a fuss of her, we haven't had a chance to talk..." Rupert is still thinking how strange everything is, when he suddenly hears music and the sound of laughter. "They must be having a banquet inside the castle!" he thinks. "I'll try to get closer and take a look. With a bit of luck the guards will be indoors now too..."

As Rupert creeps closer to the castle, he can see figures moving about inside the hall... Peering in at a window, he spots Ottoline sitting at a long table, with the Chamberlain and the rest of the Court... "They all seem very friendly!" he thinks. "I wonder what will happen when they realise that Ottoline isn't a Princess?" A Jester entertains the diners as pages carry in dishes on large wooden platters. "It looks delicious!" thinks Rupert. "I hope Ottoline manages to save some for me!"

RUPERT'S PAL IS LOCKED IN

Inside the castle, Ottoline
Is treated like a future queen...

"This way, Princess. It grows late now..."
The courtiers all turn and bow.

"Your chambers, Lady! Pray sleep tight -
I hope you have a peaceful night..."

"Don't think that you can run away -
This time, I'll make sure that you stay!"

Inside the castle, Ottoline is just as mystified as Rupert... "Everyone keeps calling me Princess!" she thinks. "I don't know why. Perhaps I fell asleep in the wood and it's all a dream..." As the meal draws to a close, the Chamberlain warns Ottoline to be more careful about where she goes. "We can't have you disappearing again!" he smiles. "Think of the commotion if you hadn't been found!" Escorting her from the table, he shows Ottoline to her room. "You must be weary after such an exciting day..."

Leading Ottoline up a winding staircase, the Chamberlain takes her along corridors hung with tapestries and rich brocade. "Here, My Lady!" he announces. "Your room awaits you..." "Thank you," smiles Ottoline. "I am rather tired, after walking so far..." "Sleep well!" says the Chamberlain. "And this time I'll make certain you don't go wandering off!" To Ottoline's astonishment, he pulls the door to and turns the key. "Goodness!" she blinks. "He's shut me in! I'm not a guest. I'm a prisoner!"

RUPERT'S CHUM MEETS HER TWIN

"Help!" Ottoline begins to shout.
"Come back at once and let me out!"

Then, suddenly, she hears a sound
Which makes her gasp and turn around...

"The real Princess!" Ottoline blinks.
"We look the same - like twins!" she thinks.

The Princess explains how she's been
Locked in, to stop her being Queen...

"Help!" calls Ottoline, tugging the handle and pounding on the door. "Let me out!" The Chamberlain gives no reply, but simply walks off, back along the corridor... "Now what?" thinks Ottoline. "I wonder why he's so keen to stop me leaving? It's a funny sort of way to treat a princess..." Just then, the sound of a muffled sneeze comes from the far side of the room. Ottoline spins round in alarm. "Somebody's there!" she gasps. "They must be hiding behind that curtain..."

To Ottoline's amazement, the curtain opens to reveal a startled figure staring back at her... "I don't believe it!" she gasps. "You look just like me!" "And you look just like me!" blinks Ottoline's double. "The Chamberlain's locked the door!" says Ottoline. "Yes," nods the Princess. "He shut me in this morning. When he saw you, he must have thought I'd got away." "Why does he keep you a prisoner?" asks Ottoline. "The Coronation!" says the Princess. "He's determined to stop me being made Queen."

RUPERT WAITS FOR NIGHTFALL

*"Tomorrow I will 'disappear' -
Kept locked up as prisoner here..."*

*"There must be something we can do!
If only Rupert was here too..."*

*Outside the castle, guards march by
As Rupert watches, like a spy.*

*"Which one can Ottoline's room be?
Perhaps she'll look out - then I'll see."*

"If I miss tomorrow's Coronation, the Chamberlain will make himself Regent!" explains the Princess. "He could keep me locked up in this tower forever!" "And me along with you!" says Ottoline. "There must be some way of escaping..." "The window's too high to climb down!" the Princess sighs. "I've tried calling for help but my room is at the back of the castle. Nobody can see us and no-one will come walking by..." "If only Rupert was here!" says Ottoline. "I'm sure he'd think of something..."

Outside the castle, Rupert waits patiently for the flickering lights of the banqueting hall to be extinguished before setting out to search for Ottoline... Creeping forward, he is nearly spotted by a pair of soldiers on patrol but manages to duck behind a bush, just in time. "That was close!" he gasps. "I wonder which window is Ottoline's? I'd better keep walking round the castle until I see her looking out. It wouldn't do to choose the wrong room and wake the Chamberlain instead!"

RUPERT MEETS A GUIDE

A cat asks "Lost your way, young man?
I'll try to help you, if I can..."

"Come on! It's easy when you know
Where things are - and which way to go."

"You see this gap? Just clamber through!
I think it's big enough for you..."

The cat fits through the hole with ease,
But Rupert finds it quite a squeeze!

As Rupert stands looking at the castle he suddenly hears a voice. "Lost your way?" it asks. At first he thinks he must have been spotted by a sentry, but, as he looks round, he is astonished to find it is a black and white cat... "I can help you, if you'd like," says the cat. "I live here. Have done ever since I was a kitten." "Thank you," blinks Rupert. "I'm looking for a friend of mine, called Ottoline..." "The Princess!" smiles the cat. "That's easy. I'll show you to her chambers..."

To Rupert's surprise, the cat walks away from the castle, towards a high wall. "Bit of a tight squeeze!" it announces. "I'll go first, then you try..." Rupert pushes slowly through a hole at the bottom of the wall. "You'll be fine so long as your whiskers fit!" calls the cat. "I haven't got any whiskers!" thinks Rupert as he emerges into a garden on the other side. "Quick as you can!" urges his guide. "I don't think there'll be another patrol but it wouldn't do for anyone to find you here."

RUPERT FINDS OTTOLINE

*"This tower's where the Princess will sleep.
Its sides are smooth and very steep..."*

*"Don't worry! You can climb a tree -
It's near enough for her to see."*

*"I heard a call!" the Princess blinks.
"It's from outside!" Ottoline thinks.*

*"Rupert!" she cries. "Thank goodness you
Have found me - and the Princess too..."*

"This is the back of the castle!" says the cat. "Princess Ottoline's room is in a high tower, far from the main gate. That window is the one you seek..." "Thank you," says Rupert. "If only the wall had more handholds! It looks too smooth to climb..." "Try the tree," suggests the cat. "You can call across to the Princess when you get to the top. The Royal apartments are normally at the front of the castle but the Chamberlain had them moved in preparation for tomorrow's coronation."

Inside the castle, Ottoline and the Princess are still discussing the Chamberlain's plan when they suddenly hear an urgent call... "Rupert!" beams Ottoline, running to the window. "He's managed to find us at last! Hello!" she waves. "I was hoping you'd come. You'll never guess what's happening..." "A Coronation," says Rupert. "I know it's meant to be tomorrow, but surely you won't be made Queen..." "Not me!" laughs Ottoline. "The real Princess is the one who should be crowned..."

*"Princess?" blinks Rupert. "Now I see!
You look like twins! Extraordinary!"*

*"She's being held a prisoner too!
We've got to help! What can we do?"*

*"I think I know! There's one last hope -
We'll use these bed-sheets as a rope..."*

*"Bravo!" cries Ottoline. "I'll stay
And hide them once you've got away."*

"The real Princess?" blinks Rupert. "Here!" says Ottoline, as a second figure appears at the window. "She's being held prisoner in her own castle!" "I thought something like this must have happened!" says Rupert. "It explains why the Chamberlain was so amazed at Ottoline being found in the woods! You've got to escape tonight, Your Highness. Nobody in the castle knows Ottoline's your double. If she stays here in your room the Chamberlain will never suspect you've gone..."

"Your friend is right!" sighs the Princess, "But how can I hope to escape from such a tall tower?" "If you had a rope you could climb across to Rupert, then clamber down the tree..." says Ottoline. "A rope!" says the Princess. "Of course! I have an idea..." Taking the sheets from her bed, the two friends knot them together, then tie one end to a bedpost. "Perfect!" smiles Ottoline. "I can pull them back in as soon as you've gone. None of the guards will ever be any the wiser."

RUPERT HELPS AN ESCAPE

Ottoline calls out to her friend -
"Get ready, Rupert! Catch the end."

"Got it!" cries Rupert happily.
"Now I'll just tie it to this tree..."

"Good luck!" cries Ottoline. "Hold tight!"
"Keep going!" Rupert calls. "That's right!"

"I'll take the Princess's place when
The Chamberlain comes back again."

As soon as the knots are securely tied, Ottoline gathers up the sheets and tosses them out of the window towards Rupert, who is waiting anxiously at the top of the tree... "Got it!" he calls triumphantly, catching hold of the end. "Now, if I can just tie them to this branch, the Princess should be able to climb across. "Hurry up!" warns Ottoline. "If the sentries come back they're bound to spot what we're up to..."   "That's it!" calls Rupert. "We're ready!"

"Good luck!" says Ottoline as the Princess slides down the makeshift rope... "Well done!" calls Rupert. "You're nearly there..." The next moment he is joined by the Princess, who steps nimbly to a nearby branch. Untying the sheets, Rupert signals to Ottoline who pulls them back into the room as fast as she can. "With a bit of luck the Chamberlain will still think you're the Princess!" he whispers. "Try to fool him a little longer, so nobody raises the alarm. A few more hours are all we need..."

RUPERT HIDES THE PRINCESS

"Where can we hide? The guards are sure
To check the castle grounds once more…"

"Don't worry!" Rupert smiles. "I know
A special way that we can go!"

"The stables!" Rupert calls. "Inside!
They'll be the perfect place to hide."

A long-forgotten carriage gleams -
"It's just what we need!" Rupert beams.

"What now?" asks the Princess. "I've escaped from the tower but I don't see how I can stop the Chamberlain from seizing the crown…" "Trust me!" smiles Rupert. "All you have to do is keep out of sight until the Coronation." "Hide?" blinks the Princess. "But where? The troops patrol all night…" "Follow me!" calls Rupert. "There's a short-cut we can take." To the Princess's amazement, he squeezes back through the hole in the wall and hurries round to the front of the castle.

"To the stables!" calls Rupert. "I'm sure the sentries won't bother us there. We can always hide in the straw if anyone comes…" As he pulls open the heavy doors, Rupert spots something glinting in the gloom… "It's my Grandfather's gold carriage!" says the Princess. "They used to use it for State occasions." "Perfect!" smiles Rupert. "Just what we need. That rascally Chamberlain of yours is in for a surprise! With Ottoline's help, we'll turn the tables yet…"

RUPERT STAYS HIDDEN

Next morning, Ottoline receives
A visitor - who she deceives...

"Farewell, Princess! Soon I'll be King -
And nobody can do a thing!"

The villagers crowd round to see
The Coronation eagerly...

The Chamberlain appears alone
And strides towards the vacant throne.

Next morning, Ottoline hears a knock at the door, followed by a key turning in the lock. "Breakfast, my dear!" announces the Chamberlain. "Such a shame you'll have to miss the Coronation but I'm sure we'll manage without you! I will be made King while you stay here..." "You can't!" stammers Ottoline. "The People won't let you..." "We'll see about that!" laughs the Chamberlain. "It will be your instructions people obey. I shall simply tell them you've asked me to govern in your place..."

Unaware of the Chamberlain's plan, the villagers gather eagerly in the castle courtyard to see Princess Ottoline's Coronation. "Quite a crowd!" murmurs Rupert. "It must be nearly time..." A trumpet sounds and then everyone falls silent as a page carries the crown to the side of a vacant throne... The Chamberlain appears, and strides towards the stage with a scroll in his hand. "Looks like a speech!" groans someone in the crowd. "Where's the Princess? Why isn't she here too?"

RUPERT FOILS THE CHAMBERLAIN

"The Princess is unwell! Instead,
The Crown will rest upon my head..."

"Wait!" Rupert calls. "The rightful Queen!
Make way for Princess Ottoline!"

"Long live the Princess!" people call.
"She's come to be crowned, after all!"

The Chamberlain is in disgrace -
"How dare you try to take my place?"

Climbing on to the stage, the Chamberlain tells the crowd that Princess Ottoline has been taken ill and is unable to leave her room... "In these unfortunate circumstances, I will rule in her place, as Regent!" he declares. Seizing the crown, he is just about to put it on when a sudden clatter of hooves fills the courtyard. "Make way!" calls Rupert, driving a golden carriage out of the stables. "Princess Ottoline is here, after all! She is in fine health and has come to claim her rightful crown..."

Overjoyed to see Princess Ottoline, the crowd starts to cheer delightedly, then everyone bows respectfully as she climbs down from the carriage... "Your...Your Highness!" gasps the Chamberlain. "How splendid to see you restored to health." "Restored," cries Rupert. "But no thanks to you!" "Arrest the Chamberlain!" orders the Princess. "His plan to seize the throne has been thwarted. My liberty has been restored and the Kingdom is saved!" "Hurrah!" cheers the crowd. "Long live the Princess!"

RUPERT CROWNS THE PRINCESS

*"One last task still remains for me -
Please step this way, Your Majesty..."*

*"Congratulations, Ottoline!"
Says Rupert. "I declare you Queen!"*

*While people cheer and call hooray,
Rupert says he must slip away...*

*He hurries up to free his friend,
"It all turned out well, in the end..."*

As the guards lead the Chamberlain away, Rupert tells Princesss Ottoline to climb up to the stage... "Let the Coronation commence!" he cries. Ottoline takes her place on the throne, then removes her crown. Taking the other crown from the waiting page boy, Rupert raises it high in the air then places it on the Princess's head. "Long live Queen Ottoline!" he calls. "Congratulations, Your Majesty!" The crowd starts to clap and cheer wildly. "Long live the Queen!" they cry.

While Queen Ottoline acknowledges the cheers of the crowd, Rupert slips away to another part of the castle... "Unfinished business!" he tells the sentry. "I need to go to the Royal apartments." Unlocking the door of the Princess's room, he finds Ottoline waiting anxiously to see how things have gone. "It worked!" Rupert laughs. "The Chamberlain has been arrested and the Princess has been crowned!" "Thank goodness!" smiles Ottoline. "I was so worried that something might go wrong..."

RUPERT AND OTTOLINE RETURN

The chums explain that they can't stay -
"We must get home without delay…"

A golden carriage takes the friends
Back home as their adventure ends.

In Nutwood, Rupert's parents stare,
Astonished as they see the pair.

"The Queen!" smiles Rupert, with a bow.
"She'll tell you all about it now…"

Thanking Rupert and Ottoline for their help, the new Queen urges them to stay for the coronation festivities. "We'd love to!" says Rupert. "But we really must get back to Nutwood. Everyone will be wondering where we are…" The Queen orders a carriage to be made ready at once. "Go with Our friendship and best wishes!" she declares. "We shall never forget all you have done…" The chums climb aboard and are soon speeding homeward, along the winding road that brought them to the castle.

Rupert's parents are amazed to see the splendid golden carriage pulling up outside their house. "It's Rupert!" gasps Mrs. Bear. "Wherever has he been?" To their surprise, Rupert jumps out of the carriage and runs around to help Ottoline down. "This way, Your Majesty!" he declares. "Majesty?" blinks Mr. Bear. "Not really!" laughs Ottoline. "But I was Princess for a day! Just wait until you hear what happened! I'm still not sure I believe it myself!"

THE END

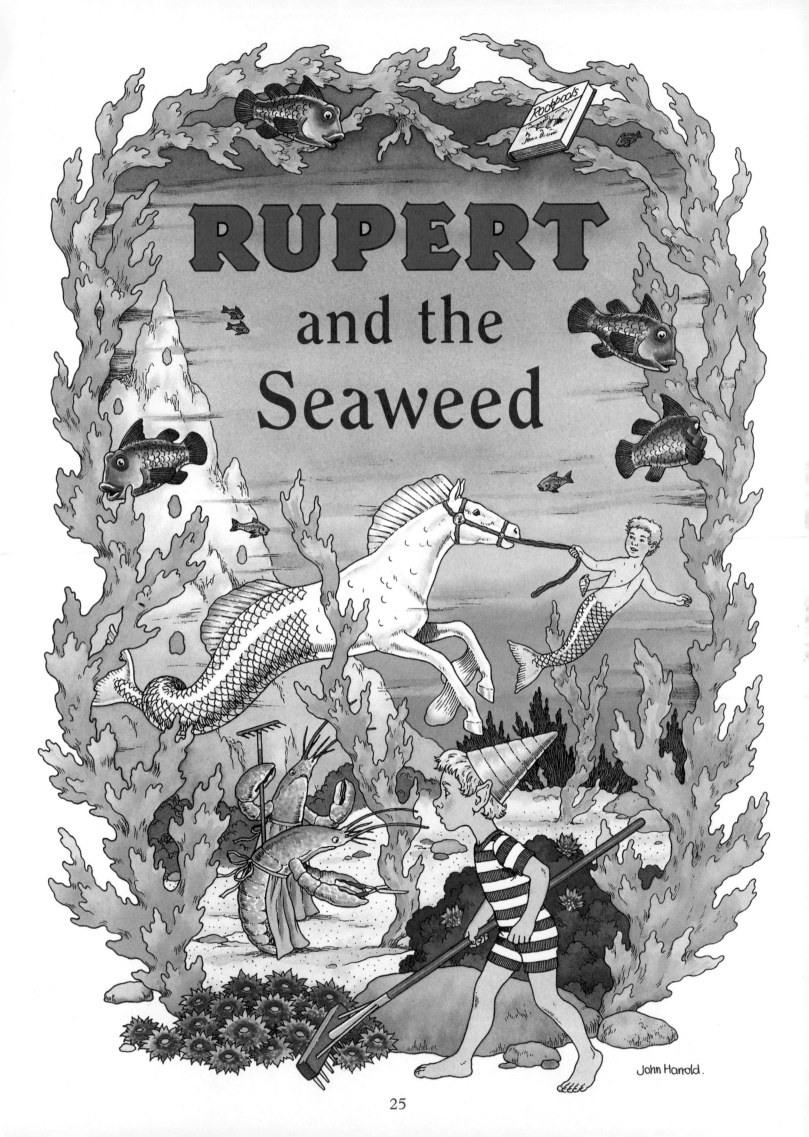

RUPERT
and the
Seaweed

John Harrold.

The Summer's here and Rupert's come
On holiday with his best chum...

The hotel's owner says hello
And shows the two friends where to go...

The pals unpack. "I've brought a book
On rock pools with me - take a look..."

"Can we go down and see the sea?"
"Of course! But don't be late for tea."

It is the start of the summer holidays. Rupert and his parents have come to Rocky Bay, together with Bill Badger... "What a lovely day!" says Mrs. Bear as they walk from the station towards their hotel. "I do hope it stays as warm as this for the rest of the week..." "It should do," nods her husband. "The forecast said we'd have sunshine." "Hello, Rupert!" smiles the landlady. "I've put you and Bill in a room just along the corridor. I'll show you the way, while your parents unpack..."

As the two chums unpack their things, Rupert shows Bill a book about rock pools which he was given at Christmas by Uncle Bruno. "It will help us identify all the things we find on the beach," he smiles. "Good!" says Bill. "Let's go and make a start straightaway..." Mrs. Bear agrees to let the pair go down to the beach while she finishes the rest of the unpacking. "Don't go too far," she warns. "Just to the water's edge and back. They'll be plenty of time tomorrow to go off exploring."

RUPERT AND BILL HEAR BAD NEWS

*"That's odd! The beach looks empty here -
It should be packed, this time of year..."*

*"The whole bay's full of seaweed too -
How very strange! It's all bright blue!"*

*"This wretched seaweed's like a curse -
Each day it just gets worse and worse!"*

*"I've never seen the stuff before -
Just started growing near the shore!"*

Rupert and Bill hurry down to the beach, only to find that it is practically deserted. "That's odd!" says Bill. "It's normally crowded at this time of year." As they step on to the sand, the pair notice something else is different too... "Seaweed!" blinks Rupert. "It's bright blue!" gasps his chum. "No wonder there aren't many people here! You can hardly see a patch of sand..." Looking out to sea, the chums are amazed by how thickly the seaweed is growing. "It's like a blanket!" says Bill.

"Ahoy, there!" calls a familiar voice. "Cap'n Binnacle," blinks Rupert. "Seaweed everywhere!" sighs the old man. "Spoils the beach for trippers, spoils the sea for fishing too! Fouls our nets and gets tangled in propellers.." The Captain says that he has never seen the blue weed before. "It just started to grow!" he shrugs. "A little at first, then more and more, until it finally smothered everything else!" "I'd better let my parents know," says Rupert. "I hope they won't decide to go home..."

*"Until the seaweed clears, we'll sit
Outside here - well away from it!"*

*The chums go back down to the shore -
"The weed looks thicker than before!"*

*No matter where the two pals go
Thick clumps of seaweed seem to grow...*

*They spot a distant group. "Let's see
If they've found somewhere that's weed-free."*

To Rupert's relief, his parents decide to stay at Rocky Bay, despite the seaweed. "We'll sit in the garden, instead of on the beach," says Mrs. Bear next morning. "You two can go and have a look, if you like. Don't be late back though, or you'll miss lunch..." The chums decide to take their buckets and nets in case they find a clear rock pool but the whole beach is still covered in bright blue weed. "It's even worse than yesterday!" says Bill. "I don't think we'll be doing much fishing."

Still searching for a clear stretch of sand, Rupert and Bill make their way along the shore away from the main beach. "It's not much better here!" shrugs Bill. "Perhaps we should just stick to playing in the garden..." "Let's try a bit further round the bay," says Rupert. "Things might be different there..." As the pair scramble over the rocks, they suddenly spot a distant group of children. "I wonder who they are?" says Rupert. "Let's go and see if they've found some clear sand..."

RUPERT AND BILL MEET TAD

"It's Tad!" cries Rupert happily.
"Hello! Do you remember me?"

The Beachcombers complain that they
Have too much weed to clear away...

"We clear the beach each day but then
The sea brings more weed in again!"

"It's odd!" says Bill. "I've never seen
Blue weed before, just brown or green..."

As they near the group, the pals see they are all wearing stripy swimming costumes and pointed, shell-like hats... "Of course!" laughs Rupert, waving his net. "It's Tad and the Beachcombers! You remember, Bill? They rake the beach each morning and gather things from the shore..." "Hello, Rupert!" says the sand sprite. "You've picked a bad time for a holiday in Rocky Bay. We're completely swamped by all this seaweed! As soon as we clear it up, another lot is carried in on the next tide..."

"I've never known anything like it!" admits Tad as the pals watch the Beachcombers clearing weed from the beach. "We should have finished our morning's work by now but everyone's been so busy with seaweed that there's hardly time for anything else!" As Tad hurries off to help the others, Bill picks up a clump of seaweed to look at it more closely. "It really is an extraordinary colour!" he says. "I've seen green weed and brown weed but never any that's bright blue."

RUPERT READS ABOUT THE SEAWEED

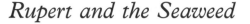

*Still mystified, the two pals look
For blue seaweed in Rupert's book.*

*"That's it!" cries Bill. "Now, does it show
Where weed like this is meant to grow?"*

*A sudden splashing shocks the pair
Who turn around to see who's there...*

*"The Merboy! Hello! How are you?"
"We're overrun with seaweed too!"*

"I wonder if there's any mention of blue weed in my book?" says Rupert. "It seems to cover most things you can find on the beach..." At first, all the pair can find are ordinary seaweeds, like bladder wrack, but as he turns the page Rupert gives a cry of triumph. "Look!" he beams. "That's the stuff!" nods Bill. "What does it say?" "It's from the South Seas," announces Rupert. "Not normally found in Northern waters..." "That's why nobody's seen it before!" says Bill. "Perhaps it was carried here by a storm?"

As they sit peering at the book, Rupert and Bill are startled by a sudden splashing from the sea... "Something's coming to the surface!" blinks Bill. "It's caught up in the weed!" "The Merboy!" gasps Rupert. "I don't suppose he's very keen on all the seaweed either..." "You can say that again!" scowls the newcomer. "It's even worse underwater than it is up here. King Neptune's gardeners have tried their best, but every time they cut the weed down it just grows back!"

RUPERT'S PAL MAKES A DISCOVERY

"Blue seaweed came in on the tide
And now it's spreading far and wide!"

"It's in my book! From the South Seas -
Not Northern latitudes, like these..."

"Look! There's a fish that eats blue weed!
A shoal of them is what we need!"

"You're right!" the Merboy blinks. "If we
Had fish like that they'd clear the sea!"

Climbing out of the water, the Merboy tells Rupert and Bill how blue seaweed first appeared in Rocky Bay... "It just seemed to spring up overnight!" he says. "Nobody knows where it came from..." "We do!" says Rupert. "It's here in my book on Rock Pools..." The Merboy blinks in amazement as he looks at the picture. "From the South Seas!" he blinks. "Who would have guessed it? I wonder if it causes such a problem there? I've never known seaweed spread so quickly..."

Leafing through the pages of Rupert's book, Bill looks for more information on the South Seas... "Listen!" he cries. "Blue weed is the favourite food of a fish called the Pink Nibbler! Shoals of Nibblers are to be found wherever the blue weed grows!" "Of course!" gasps the Merboy. "The fish must stop it from spreading and getting out of control. King Neptune must hear about this! If only we had Pink Nibblers here! They'd have a feast! No one else seems to like eating blue weed."

RUPERT SEES NEPTUNE'S BUBBLE

The Merboy blows a shell to sound
A note which echoes all around.

In answer to his urgent call
A dolphin springs up, with a ball...

"This bubble is designed to show
Land-dwellers the sea, down below."

"It's made from glass that's crystal clear
And acts just like a bathysphere."

Delighted by the pals' discovery, the Merboy tells them they must show King Neptune straightaway. Blowing on a sea-shell trumpet, he sends a long, loud note echoing around the bay. As the sound dies away, Rupert sees the water swell, then erupt with an enormous splash... "A dolphin!" blinks Bill. To the chums' astonishment the creature balances a large, transparent ball on its nose, which it pushes over the waves in response to the Merboy's summons...

"Just what we need!" beams the Merboy. "Neptune's bubble..." "It's made of glass," gasps Rupert. "Exactly!" smiles his friend. "We created it specially for land-dwellers, like you..." Releasing a catch, the Merboy shows the chums how the ball opens. "Hop in!" he cries. "There's plenty of room for two..." Rupert steps into the bottom half of the bubble, while the waiting dolphin holds it steady. "Well done!" calls the Merboy. "Your turn next, Bill. Then we'll be all set."

RUPERT GOES BENEATH THE WAVES

The Merboy dives in. "Follow me!"
Down to the bottom of the sea..."

The pals look round, amazed to find
Bright-coloured fish of every kind.

"There's Neptune's Palace!" Rupert blinks.
"It's surrounded by weed!" he thinks...

The gardeners are in despair -
"Blue weed is growing everywhere!"

When the chums are safely inside, the Merboy closes the lid of the bubble and dives back into the sea. "Follow me!" he calls. "I'll take you straight to Neptune's garden..." Rupert and Bill are amazed as the dolphin pushes them down through fronds of seaweed and shoals of brightly-coloured fish. "It's like being in a submarine!" laughs Bill. "Or wearing a diving suit!" says Rupert. "I can see everything so clearly it feels as though we're swimming. I wonder how far it is to Neptune's Palace?"

As the bubble sinks deeper and deeper Rupert and Bill suddenly spot a rocky mound rising up from the ocean floor. "King Neptune's castle!" blinks Bill. The Merboy swims on, towards a mass of colourful seaweed. "Those must be the Palace grounds!" says Rupert. "There's the King. He's surrounded by a group of crabs and lobsters." "The Royal gardeners!" calls the Merboy. "They've been working overtime, trying to control the blue weed, but it's still smothering all the other plants..."

"No guests!" snaps Neptune. "Not today!
Please tell them both to go away…"

"We've come about the blue seaweed –
I think we've found the thing you need."

King Neptune blinks. "You're right! Bless me!
A task for Nibblers! I agree!"

The King asks Rupert if he'll go
To where the blue weed's said to grow…

"Visitors, Sire!" calls the Merboy as King Neptune catches sight of the bubble. "They've come from Rocky Bay…" "Really!" snaps the King. "I'm afraid I'm too busy dealing with this dratted weed to entertain guests!" "It's the blue weed we've come about!" says Rupert. "I think I know a way to clear it all away…" "You do?" blinks Neptune. "Yes", smiles Rupert. "It's here in my book. Pink Nibblers! That's what Rocky Bay needs. They eat blue weed all the time…"

King Neptune looks at the pictures in Rupert's book. "Nibblers!" he blinks. "I should have thought of those before. A shoal from the South Seas would soon clear the weed…" The King thinks hard, then asks Rupert if he and Bill would go on a special mission… "I'll send you by sea-horse!" he explains. "The fish live near a remote group of islands, far from the world of men. They're not used to visitors, but when you explain why they're needed, I'm sure they'll agree to help."

RUPERT RIDES A SEAHORSE

*The Merboy leads a special steed
That's famous for its strength and speed...*

*"This horse is one that Neptune saves
To carry him across the waves."*

*"Let Hippocampus find the way -
He'll take you anywhere you say..."*

*As soon as Rupert speaks, the horse
Speeds off upon its chosen course.*

The chums are thrilled by the sight of the strange horse and readily agree to help fetch a shoal of nibblers. "Good luck!" calls Neptune as the dolphin pushes them back to the surface. "From this moment you are Our special emissaries..." The Merboy follows the pair with the sea-horse, which speeds through the water with a few powerful sweeps of its tail. "You'll be the first land-dwellers to ride Neptune's steed!" he smiles. "He's called Hippocampus, the swiftest creature in all the seven seas..."

Stepping out of the bubble, Rupert and Bill climb carefully on to the back of the sea-horse... "Don't worry!" says the Merboy as he hands Rupert the reins. "He's been trained by Neptune himself. Just let him have his head and he'll take you wherever you want to go..." Rupert leans forward and whispers in the horse's ear. "Speed Hippocampus, if you please, to find blue weed in the South Seas!" The horse nods its head and, with a flick of its tail, speeds straight out to sea.

RUPERT GOES ON A JOURNEY

The pals ride on and quickly find
They've left all sight of land behind...

"Look, Rupert!" Bill cries. "Over there!"
"An island!" cheer the hopeful pair.

The pals draw near and find they're wrong -
The "islands" were whales all along!

The sea-horse speeds on till they see
Another island - could it be?

Hippocampus gallops across the sea so quickly that Rupert and Bill have soon left Rocky Bay far behind. Clinging on to his back, they wonder how far they have come and how much further they have to go... "Land ahoy!" calls Bill suddenly. "I can see a group of islands on the horizon." "You're right!" says Rupert. "I can see them too. We seem to be heading straight towards them. Perhaps they're where the blue weed grows? I hope we'll find Pink Nibblers there too..."

As they draw nearer, the pals are amazed to see that what they took to be a group of islands is actually a school of whales basking in the sunshine... At the sight of the sea-horse, they each spout water and splash the sea with their tails. Hippocampus neighs a greeting, but carries on without slackening speed. The next time the pals spot land they are sure they must be nearing their destination. "I can see trees and shrubs," says Bill. "It won't be long before we're there..."

RUPERT IS STOPPED BY A SERPENT

*"This looks just right! Let's go ashore
And find the weed we're looking for..."*

*The sea-horse gives a startled neigh -
A huge sea-serpent blocks the way!*

*The serpent speaks - "Pray, who are you?
What is it you have come to do?"*

*At Neptune's name it lets them by -
"Blue seaweed!" Bill hears Rupert cry...*

Nearing the island, Rupert and Bill see it is completely overgrown with trees and tangled vegetation which grows right down to the shore. "Far from the world of men..." says Rupert. "It's uninhabited, so I suppose everything just runs wild." As he speaks, the sea-horse suddenly rears up, whinnying in alarm. To the pals' dismay they see the way is blocked by a fearsome looking sea-serpent. "What now?" blinks Bill. "It doesn't seem very pleased to see us!"

"Who are you?" asks the sea-serpent. "Why do you disturb the peace of this island?" "I...I'm sorry if we startled you," says Rupert. "We've been sent here by King Neptune. He's asked us to find a shoal of Pink Nibblers..." "Neptune?" blinks the serpent. "Then pass and be welcome. His Majesty's writ runs far and wide!" Hippocampus swims on towards the shore. Looking down, Rupert suddenly gives an excited cry. "Bill! The seaweed here is bright blue! I'm sure we're in the right place for Pink Nibblers..."

RUPERT SEES SOME PINK NIBBLERS

*"Look, Bill! There's just the fish we need –
A Pink Nibbler, which eats blue weed..."*

*Rupert tells the Nibbler he knows
Where lots of bright blue seaweed grows...*

*A shoal of Nibblers come to say
That they will swim to Rocky Bay.*

*"We'll lead the way across the sea!"
Calls Rupert. "Follow Bill and me!"*

As the chums look down, they see a brightly-coloured fish swimming through the blue weed. "A Nibbler!" cries Rupert. "We've found one at last..." Climbing on to a large rock, he kneels down and calls to the fish. When the Nibbler hears what has happened, it soon agrees to help the pals. "Blue weed's our favourite food!" it smiles. "You might not want it at Rocky Bay but my friends and I can never have too much!" "Come back with us!" says Rupert. "Tell all your friends they'll be in for a feast..."

The fish swims off and quickly returns with a whole shoal of Pink Nibblers, who seem delighted at the prospect of a trip to Rocky Bay... "When do we start?" calls one. "I like the sound of all this weed!" "Can I come?" asks another. "Me too!" cries a third. "You'll all be welcome!" announces Rupert. "The more the merrier. I want you to clear the whole bay!" When the fish are all ready, Rupert climbs on to Hippocampus and asks the sea-horse to lead the way."

RUPERT LEADS THE WAY

The sea-horse knows which route to take
And leads the Nibblers in its wake...

At last the pals see land once more -
"It's Rocky Bay!" cries Bill. "I'm sure."

The Nibblers start to eat their fill -
"They're hungry from their swim!" says Bill.

The Merboy waves and starts to cheer
As he sees the two pals draw near...

The sea-horse sets off across the sea with a great shoal of Pink Nibblers following behind... "It's like the Pied Piper in reverse!" laughs Bill. "I hope the journey isn't too exhausting for them!" says Rupert. "It's a long way to Rocky Bay..." As if to reassure the chums, Hippocampus slows down from time to time until the slowest Nibblers have caught up. "Land ahoy!" calls Bill at last. "It's Rocky Bay!" he laughs. "Not long now, then the Nibblers can have the meal of their lives!"

As soon as they reach Rocky Bay, the Pink Nibblers start devouring blue seaweed as fast as they can... "Tuck in!" laughs Rupert. "I hope you enjoy it!" "Thanks!" calls the Nibblers' leader. "This is delicious weed. Some of the best I've ever tasted..." Leaving the fish to their meal, Rupert and Bill ride in towards the shore where they soon spot the Merboy basking on a rock. "Well done!" he calls. "I see you found the Nibblers! Might have known you wouldn't let us down!"

RUPERT'S PLAN WORKS

*"I'll tell the King how well you've done
And that the Nibblers have begun."*

*The Bears are pleased the weed has gone -
"In that case we can all stay on..."*

*Next morning, Rupert goes to see -
The whole beach seems to be weed-free.*

*"It disappeared! I don't know how -
But everyone is happy now..."*

When the chums have climbed down from the sea-horse, the Merboy takes Hippocampus' reins and prepares to return to King Neptune. "His Majesty will be delighted!" he smiles. "When the Nibblers have finished feasting I'll take them all home..." Mrs. Bear is also pleased to hear that the seaweed is going. "If the beach is back to normal we can all look forward to a nice week in the sun..." "Everything will be fine now," says Rupert. "By tomorrow you'll never know that anything was ever wrong."

The next day, Rupert and his parents go down to the beach as soon as they have finished breakfast... "Hello there!" calls Cap'n Binnacle as they join him on the sand. "Good seaws for holiday makers! The blue seaweed has vanished! Blessed stuff just disappeared as mysteriously as it came..." "Good riddance!" says Mr. Bear. "I wonder where it went?" "I wonder?" says Rupert, winking at Bill. "There's something fishy about all this, if you ask me." "Very fishy!" laughs Bill. "Very fishy indeed..."

THE END

RUPERT's
Birthday Adventure

John Harrold.

RUPERT MEETS COUSIN BEA

When Rupert's birthday comes he sends
Out invitations to his friends...

"I do hope everybody comes -
I want to play with all my chums!"

As Rupert nears the post-box he
Sees Bill, who's with his cousin Bea...

"Hello, Bill! This invite's for you -
Please bring your little cousin too."

It is Autumn in Nutwood and nearly time for Rupert's birthday. He and Mrs. Bear have been planning a special party and are busy writing invitations to all his chums. "I hope I haven't forgotten anybody!" says Rupert. "Check the names on your list," smiles his mother. "There are so many there I think you must have invited the whole class..." When the final invitation has been written, Rupert sticks stamps on all the envelopes and sets out towards the High Street to post them straightaway.

As Rupert nears the postbox he spots his pal Bill Badger, coming towards him with a new companion... "Hello!" says Bill. "This is my cousin, Beatrix. She's visiting Nutwood for the first time and will be staying with us for the whole week..." "Pleased to meet you!" smiles Rupert. "If you're staying all week you'll be able to come to my birthday party too!" "Yes, please!" squeaks the little badger. "Good idea!" smiles Bill. "She's only three but I'm sure she'll enjoy meeting all the others..."

RUPERT'S PARTY BEGINS

"At last! It's time!" The guests begin
Arriving. Rupert lets them in…

"It's Bea! Come in and join the fun -
You'll soon get to know everyone!"

"We'll have a treasure hunt! Look round!
All sorts of prizes to be found…"

"Ah, ha!" laughs Bill, then gives a cheer.
"Look, Bea! I think I've found one here."

For the rest of the week Rupert looks forward excitedly to the day of his party. To everyone's delight the weather stays fine, with autumn sunshine brightening the whole house. "Happy birthday!" cries Tigerlily as Rupert opens the door. "Am I the first one here?" More guests appear and by the time that Bill and Beatrix arrive the room is full of Nutwood pals, all chatting happily. "Hello, you two!" calls Rupert. "Come in and I'll introduce Beatrix to everyone else…"

As it is such a fine, sunny day, Mrs. Bear suggests that the chums might like to play in the garden while she prepares their tea. "I've organised a treasure hunt!" she tells them. "There should be enough prizes for everyone, but you'll have to look very carefully to find them all…" Rupert's guests start to search the garden excitedly. "I think I've found something!" calls Willie, reaching under a bush. "And what's this?" laughs Bill. "Look, Beatrix! We've found something too…"

RUPERT HAS A VISITOR

"Look, in the sky!" cries Ottoline.
The others peer at what she's seen.

"It's the Balloonist!" Rupert cries,
A friend the pals all recognise...

"Hello, I've brought a birthday gift
And come to offer you a lift."

"A flying helmet!" Rupert beams.
He's going for a flight it seems...

Rupert is still helping his chums search for prizes when he suddenly sees Ottoline, pointing up at the sky... "Look!" she cries. "A huge balloon!" "It's coming down!" gasps Edward. "I can see the pilot waving." "The Balloonist!" laughs Rupert, recognising his old friend. "He promised he'd come back to Nutwood one day..." "Hello!" calls the Balloonist as he lands on the lawn. "Hope you don't mind me dropping in like this! I was flying nearby and thought I'd come and wish Rupert a happy birthday!"

As the chums gather round, the Balloonist reaches into his basket and produces a small parcel. "For you!" he tells Rupert. "I hope it's the right size..." Rupert unwraps the present excitedly. "A flying helmet!" he cries. "How wonderful! It's just like yours..." "Actually, that's only the first part of the present," the Balloonist tells Mrs. Bear. "I really wondered if Rupert fancied a jaunt over Nutwood? Spot of sight-seeing - perhaps just as far as the Professor's tower..."

RUPERT GETS READY FOR A FLIGHT

*"That's just the ticket! We're all set -
I'll hold the basket, in you get..."*

*"Bea too!" calls Beatrix. "Bea want fly!
In big balloon up in the sky!"*

*"I don't see why she shouldn't come!
We'll take her and one other chum..."*

*"We won't be long! A little hop
To see the village, then we'll stop."*

Mrs. Bear says she's happy for Rupert to go up in the balloon, so long as he doesn't leave the party for too long. "No, no!" laughs the Balloonist. "If we leave straightaway we'll be back in a jiffy..." Rupert fastens his helmet and gets ready to climb into the basket. "All set!" smiles the Balloonist, then spins round with a cry of surprise. "I say! Who's this?" "Bea!" cries Beatrix. "Bea fly too!" "Oh dear!" says Bill. "I think she wants to join you..."

The Balloonist picks Beatrix up for a closer look. "You're a bit small for ballooning!" he laughs. "Still, I don't see why you shouldn't try.... Your brother could come along too! There's bags of room inside the basket!" Bill is delighted at a chance to join Rupert for an unexpected balloon ride and promises to make sure his cousin is safe and sound. "No need for alarm, Mrs. Bear!" says the Balloonist. "We'll simply float gently over Nutwood, then come back down to land where we started..."

RUPERT TAKES OFF SUDDENLY

Inside the basket, Bea looks round
Then pulls a lever that she's found...

"Stop!" Rupert calls, but it's too late.
"I say!" the Balloonist gasps. "Wait!"

"Come back!" calls Mrs. Bear. "Oh, my!
They're sailing up into the sky..."

"The lever won't turn back again...
That means we'll go on climbing then."

Rupert, Bill and Beatrix wait in the basket while the Balloonist says goodbye to Mrs. Bear. Bill's cousin is so excited that she keeps jumping up and down, trying to peer over the edge. Before Bill can stop her, she grabs hold of a lever and swings on it with a cry of glee. "Don't!" gasps Rupert. "That works the controls..." As he speaks, the basket suddenly starts to sway. "What's happening? Help! I say!" cries the Balloonist, tumbling to the ground. "Don't take off without me!"

Rupert and Bill feel the balloon give a sudden lurch, then rise swiftly above the astonished guests. "Come back!" cries Mrs. Bear but it is already too late... The balloon floats higher and higher over the garden until the figures below look tiny. "I can't turn the lever back!" gasps Bill. "It seems to be jammed..." "Bea flying!" comes a voice from the basket. "At least Beatrix isn't frightened!" says Rupert. "I am!" says Bill. "If we keep on climbing we'll go through the clouds!"

RUPERT FLIES AWAY

*The pals keep climbing till they see
Thick cloud all round. "I'm cold!" says Bea.*

*A sudden strong wind starts to blow -
The pals leave Nutwood far below...*

*At last, they wrench the lever free -
"Now we can come down gradually."*

*The pals descend, to find that they
Must have been carried miles away...*

Sure enough, the balloon keeps climbing until it is completely engulfed in chilly mist. "Brrrr!" shivers Beatrix. "Bea cold!" To the pals' relief, they soon emerge above the clouds, where the sun is shining brightly. "That's better!" laughs Bill. "At least we'll be warm." "We would be if it wasn't so windy!" calls Rupert. "I think we're in for a gale..." As he speaks a strong gust catches the balloon and sends it speeding through the sky. "Gosh!" blinks Bill. "I'd no idea balloons went so fast!"

Buffeted by the wind, the balloon finally slows to a halt as Rupert wrenches the control lever free. "Well done!" calls Bill. "Now we can try to land..." Drifting gently down through a thick layer of cloud, the pals peer over the basket at an unfamiliar landscape of trees and rocky hills. "Where are we?" blinks Bill. "I don't know," says Rupert. "We've been blown over Nutwood and beyond the far side of the forest. We must have drifted for miles and miles..."

"Look, there!" Bill gives a startled cry.
"Another balloon in the sky!"

The chums wave to the pilot. "He
Might know which way Nutwood can be..."

A strong wind blows, the chums fly on,
It seems their only hope has gone!

Then, suddenly, the pals see more
Balloons. "Where are they heading for?"

To Bill's astonishment he suddenly spots another balloon, floating nearby. "Look!" he cries. "It's coming towards us!" As the balloon gets closer, the chums wave to attract the pilot's attention. "He'll be able to tell us where we are!" says Rupert. "With a bit of luck he might know the way back to Nutwood..." "Hello!" calls Bill. "I wonder if you can help us?" "I say!" gasps Rupert. "The Balloonist!" "That's who I'm calling to!" says Bill. "No, our Balloonist!" says Rupert. "The pilot looks just like him!"

The pilot of the second balloon turns to the pals and waves but, before he can say anything, a sudden gust of wind sends them racing on ahead. "We'll just have to hope he catches up soon!" shrugs Bill. "He must have borrowed another balloon and come all the way from Nutwood to look for us..." As the chums glance back, they are amazed to see more balloons appear - all flying in the same direction. "I don't understand!" blinks Rupert. "I wonder if he's organised a search party?"

RUPERT GAINS AN ESCORT

*Two storks appear. "A splendid race -
You've really set a cracking pace!"*

*"Don't slow down now! You're in the lead -
Just keep on flying at full speed!"*

*The pals continue on their flight -
A great castle comes into sight...*

*The pair of storks swoop down to land
Where birds of every kind all stand.*

Rupert and Bill are still staring at the cluster of balloons when a sudden cry makes them spin round in surprise. Two enormous storks hover nearby, beating the air with their wings. "Ahoy there!" cries the first bird. "You're the first balloon we've seen!" "Hello!" stammers Rupert. "I wonder if you can tell us the way back to Nutwood?" "Back?" squawks the bird incredulously. "You don't want to go back! You're in the lead! I don't think any of the others will catch up with you now..."

As the storks fly on ahead, Rupert and Bill realise that they have accidentally entered a giant balloon race... "And we're in the lead!" marvels Bill. The next minute the pals spot a far-off castle, perched high on one of the rocky peaks. "Look, Bill!" cries Rupert. "It's surrounded by birds! Just like the Bird King's Palace..." As they near the castle the pair see the storks swoop gracefully down to greet a court official. "The end of the race!" gasps Rupert. "I think we're meant to land there too!"

"Our journey's over!" Rupert calls.
The balloon stops, then slowly falls...

"Bravo!" the birds call, flocking round
As the basket lands on the ground.

"Well done! A splendid victory!
It will delight His Majesty..."

"The King approves of balloons! They're
The quietest manned craft in the air!"

Rupert pulls sharply at the balloon's controls as they hover over the terrace. "Bea landing!" calls Beatrix as the basket starts to fall. "Not too fast!" warns Bill but by lifting the lever gradually, Rupert manages to touch down with only a gentle bump. "Bravo!" cry the excited birds. "Three cheers for the winners!" "I say!" blinks Rupert. "That's the Bird King's Chamberlain. I wonder if the King is here too? He doesn't normally approve of anyone flying, except for birds..."

To Rupert's surprise, the Chamberlain seems delighted and hurries forward to offer his congratulations... "Well done!" he smiles. "A memorable victory. His Majesty will be pleased!" "Thank you," blinks Rupert. "But I thought the King didn't like people flying..." "That's because he hates noisy machines," explains the courtier. "Balloons are different. Silent, graceful, skillfully flown. His Majesty runs an annual balloon race in the hope of encouraging more pilots to take it up..."

RUPERT WINS A PRIZE

"It's the Balloonist!" Rupert blinks.
"He must have followed us!" he thinks.

A trumpet blows. The King appears.
"A wonderful result!" he cheers.

The Bird King meets the winning crew -
"My goodness! Rupert Bear! It's you..."

"Well done!" another pilot beams.
"You left us all behind, it seems..."

As more birds gather round to see the winners, Rupert spots a fleet of other balloonists, gliding gently down to join them... "There's our chum!" he cries. "I hope he won't mind us stealing his prize! First we make off in his balloon, then a sudden gust of wind puts us out in the lead..." To the pals' relief, the Balloonist doesn't seem at all put out at being runner up. He waves back to Rupert but before they can speak a trumpeter announces the Bird King's arrival...

The Bird King takes a gleaming cup and prepares to present it to the winning crew... "Rupert!" he blinks. "Young Rupert Bear, from Nutwood. I didn't know you went ballooning..." "I don't! I mean, I haven't, very often." says Rupert. "This is the first race Bill and I have ever entered..." "Beginners' luck, then!" laughs the King. "Still, you won the trophy, fair and square!" "Quite right!" calls another balloonist. "First rate flying! Saw it all as I followed you here..."

*Next moment, the Balloonist comes -
"Bravo!" he cries and greets the chums.*

*"I'll just jot down your names! Please tell
Me yours first, then your friends' as well..."*

*"We met this morning! When you flew
To Nutwood! You met Bill there too..."*

*"Nutwood? I recognise the name,
But I've not been there, all the same..."*

As the other competitors gather round to congratulate Rupert and Bill, their friend, the Balloonist, comes hurrying over the join them. "Bravo!" he smiles. "Thought I'd almost caught up there, then that last minute dash left me standing..." To the chums' surprise, he makes no mention of the mishap that sent them on their way but takes out a notebook and asks Rupert to spell his name. "For the Ballooning Gazette!" he laughs. "They always like a detailed report of who won..."

The two chums are astonished by the Balloonist's question... "You already know who I am!" blinks Rupert. "This is my friend, Bill Badger and his cousin, Beatrix. We'd never have been on a balloon ride if you hadn't landed in Nutwood and come to visit my party..." As Rupert speaks, it is the Balloonist's turn to look mystified... "Nutwood?" he murmurs. "Nut as in hazel and wood as in tree? It sounds familiar, but I don't think I've ever been there. There must be some mistake..."

RUPERT SOLVES THE MYSTERY

"We flew away in your balloon!
You can't have forgotten so soon…"

"My brother, Hector! He must be
The one you mean. Looks just like me."

"You're Rupert Bear! My brother's friend –
I'm glad the mystery's at an end!"

"The balloon race was fun but how
Can we get back to Nutwood now?"

Rupert is dumbfounded. "You can't have forgotten everything that happened…" he protests. "You visited Nutwood earlier today and gave Bill and me a ride in your balloon! That's how we came to join the race…" "My balloon?" blinks the pilot, then he suddenly smiles. "Of course! I know what's caused the confusion. This isn't mine. It belongs to my brother, Hector! We're both balloonists, you see. He's the one who told me about Nutwood. Got a friend there called Rudolph, I think…"

"That's me!" laughs Rupert. "Only my name's not Rudolph! I met your brother when his balloon came down on Nutwood common. I didn't know there were two of you…" "We're twins!" explains the stranger. "My name's Horace!" Rupert explains how the chums came to be cast adrift in the balloon. "Astonishing!" he blinks. "And you went on to win the race…" "That's all very well," says Rupert. "But what we really want to do is get back to Nutwood. Everyone will be terribly worried if we're not home soon!"

*"The only way to travel back
Is wait till the wind changes tack!"*

*A marshal waves a flag to show
The wind has changed. It's time to go...*

*"Stand by to cast off! In you hop –
We'll fly to Nutwood now, non-stop..."*

*The Bird King waves and calls "Goodbye!"
As the balloons take to the sky.*

When the Bird King hears how Rupert and Bill are keen get back to Nutwood, he shakes his head and shrugs. "That's the only drawback to balloons, I'm afraid. They can only travel in the same direction as the wind! You'll have to wait until it changes..." "But that could take ages!" groans Bill. "We might be here for days!" As he speaks, a marshal appears with a brightly coloured flag. "Attention all balloonists!" he calls. "The wind is turning, from East to West!"

"Time you were off!" declares Horace. He helps Rupert and Bill clamber into their basket then lifts Beatrix gently over the side. "A Westerly wind should be perfect!" he smiles. "You'll be back in Nutwood no time at all..." "What if we miss it?" asks Bill. "Don't worry!" laughs Horace. "I'm sure it's on my map..." "Your map?" asks Rupert. "Yes!" beams Horace. "I've decided to come too!" "Goodbye!" calls the Bird King as the balloons take off. "Congratulations on winning the race!"

RUPERT RETURNS TO NUTWOOD

The chums keep Horace well in sight -
"Straight on!" he calls. "The wind's just right!"

At last! A sight the chums both know -
"It's Nutwood! Almost straight below..."

"I'll pull the lever slowly, then
We should go safely down again."

In Rupert's garden, all his friends
Call out as the balloon flight ends...

The two balloons are soon carried off by a stiff Westerly breeze, leaving the Bird King and his Court officials far behind... "I wonder if we're still going in the right direction?" says Bill. "I can't see any landmarks I recognise..." As if to answer his question, Horace looks up from his map reading and points excitedly ahead... "Nutwood!" cries Rupert. "Look, Bill. I can see the church tower and all the houses of the village. It won't be long before we're right overhead!"

Rupert waits until the balloon is directly above his garden, then pulls the control lever to send it gently down..." Bea back!" cries Beatrix happily. "Yes!" smiles Bill. "Just wait till all the others hear where we've been..." As the balloon comes down to land, Rupert spots his chums all peering up excitedly. "Well done!" calls the old Professor. "I saw you approaching through my telescope. It's lucky the wind changed direction or who knows where you would have landed?"

RUPERT LANDS SAFELY

*"Thank goodness!" Mrs. Bear cries. "We
Had no idea where you could be!"*

*"All's well that ends well!" Horace cries.
"These youngsters even won a prize!"*

*"Congratulations, Mrs. Bear!
Your son's team beat us, fair and square!"*

*Then Rupert sees that Bea has stayed
Behind. "What's wrong? She looks dismayed..."*

The balloon lands perfectly and Rupert is soon telling his mother all about the unexpected journey and how he and Bill won a special race. "Thank goodness you're back safely!" declares Mrs. Bear. "The Professor was all ready to go and look for you in one of his flying machines!" "No need, by the look of things!" smiles Hector. "But tell me more about the race. The Bird King's Cup is a trophy I've always wanted to win..." "Me too!" calls Horace as he glides down to join the others...

Hector is delighted to see his brother and soon introduces him to all the party guests. "We're both keen balloonists he tells Mrs. Bear. "Capital sport!" nods Horace. "Particularly when it brings you to such charming places..." Hector insists on hearing how the pals followed the marshals to the Bird King's palace. "We didn't even know it was a race!" says Bill. Rupert is just about to join them when he notices Beatrix, peering fearfully out from behind a basket...

RUPERT GETS A BIRTHDAY CAKE

"Don't worry!" Rupert laughs. "I'm sure
That he won't be cross any more…"

"An accident!" smiles Hector. "You
Know, I once did the same thing too!"

As Hector hears of Rupert's ride
He carries little Bea inside…

"Three cheers for Rupert, Bill and Bea!"
Says Rupert's mother. "Time for tea!"

Rupert kneels down to talk to Bill's cousin. "Whatever's the matter?" he asks. "Loonist cross!" she sniffs. "Bea make loon fly…" "Don't worry!" smiles Rupert. "Hector won't be cross. He knows you didn't mean to make the balloon go without him…" "Rather!" smiles the Balloonist, hoisting Beatrix up for a chat. "All an accident. It could have happened to anyone! Once did the same thing myself, come to think of it. Up in the clouds before I knew what was happening…"

Hector carries Beatrix indoors to join the rest of the party guests. "I'm jolly glad to see you all back safe and sound!" he says. "Winning that cup was a stroke of good fortune too! Horace and I have been after it for ages…" "Richly deserved!" beams his brother. "First-rate flying! Rupert, Bill and Beatrix must be the youngest champions ever!" "Happy birthday, dear!" says Mrs. Bear as she brings in Rupert's cake. "You certainly seem to have had an exciting party!"

RUPERT and

*Rupert wonders if Pong-Ping might
Agree to help him fly his kite...*

It is a fine sunny morning and Rupert is on his way to visit Pong-Ping... "I hope he likes my new kite!" he thinks. "I haven't had a chance to fly it yet, but the weather today looks perfect..." As he reaches Pong-Ping's house, Rupert spots his chum's pet dragon, Ming, who comes scampering up the path to greet him. "Hello!" he smiles. "I hope your master's free. He's just the person to take on a kite-flying expedition..."

the Pearl Fishers

*"Hello, Ming! Is your Master there?
I've brought a kite to fly somewhere…"*

*"I can't go flying kites today -
I'm off to China, straightaway…"*

To Rupert's disappointment, Pong-Ping is too busy to come kite-flying. "I'd love to," says his chum, "But I've just had an urgent message from China. It's been sent by Li-Poo, the Emperor's chamberlain. He needs help and wants me to come and join him straightaway…" "What's wrong?" blinks Rupert. "I don't know," admits the Peke. "The message doesn't give any details. A matter of great importance is all he says. I'd better go as quickly as I can…"

*"Li-Poo has sent a note to me -
He says it's an emergency!"*

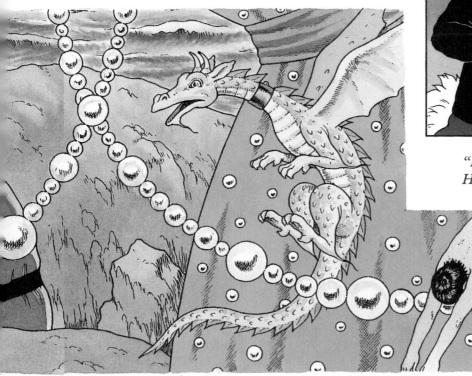

RUPERT GOES TO CHINA

*"There must be something I can do...
Why don't I come to China too?"*

*Pong-Ping agrees. "We'll set off now -
By private lift - I'll show you how..."*

*"Hold tight!" calls Pong-Ping. "Here we go!
Full speed to China, down below..."*

*The lift swings round. "It won't be long,"
Says Pong-Ping. "Then we'll see what's wrong!"*

Rupert is just about to say goodbye to Pong-Ping when he suddenly has a good idea... "I could come with you!" he suggests. "Two heads are always better than one." "I...I suppose you're right!" nods the Peke. "We can go together in my private lift. It won't take us long to reach the Royal Palace. Li-Poo can explain what's wrong and why he had to send such an urgent message. I'm sure he won't mind you joining me. It sounds as though he needs all the help he can get!"

As Rupert knows, Pong-Ping has a special lift which goes all the way from Nutwood to the Emperor's Palace in China. "Hold tight!" he warns. "I've set the controls to full speed!" The pals hear a hum of machinery then find themselves hurtling down through a deep, dark tunnel. "Get ready for a change in direction," calls the Peke. Rupert manages to keep his feet but Ming is taken by surprise and goes tumbling as the lift tilts abruptly. "Not long now!" says his master. "We'll soon be arriving in China!"

RUPERT'S PAL HAS A MESSAGE

*The pals arrive. "Quick! Follow me!
We'll find what the trouble can be..."*

*An old man greets the chums. "Li-Poo
Told me he was expecting you."*

*"I don't know how much you have heard –
A grave misfortune has occurred."*

*"Li-Poo awaits you urgently.
He's at the Palace by the Sea..."*

As the lift stops moving, Pong-Ping leads the way out through the gardens of the Emperor's Palace. "Follow me!" he calls. "We'll find Li-Poo and ask him what's wrong..." To the Peke's surprise, the Palace seems deserted. No guards patrol the grounds and the only figure the friends can see is an old man, sitting at a table in the courtyard. "Pong-Ping!" he blinks as they approach. "My brother said you would come. Arrangements have been made for you to join him without delay..."

"Li-Poo is at the Emperor's Summer Palace," explains the old man. "The whole court travels to the coast each year, leaving only a few of us behind to guard the Royal Chambers. If only His Excellency had remained too, then all would still be well..." "The Emperor?" blinks Pong-Ping. "Li-Poo will explain," sighs the courtier. "A terrible calamity has befallen us! My brother thinks that you might be able to help. A carriage will take you to the Summer Palace straightaway..."

"Each year, the Emperor goes to stay
By the sea for a holiday…"

"The Summer Palace!" Rupert blinks.
"It looks magnificent!" he thinks.

Li-Poo appears. "I've sent for you
Because I don't know what to do…"

"Some kidnappers came yesterday
And took the Emperor away!"

"I wonder what's happened?" asks Rupert as the carriage sets off along a winding road through the hills. "Something to do with the Emperor!" says Pong-Ping. "His holiday at the Summer Palace is normally very relaxed. Affairs of state are forgotten while everyone enjoys the sun. There must be a serious problem for Li-Poo to send a message all the way to Nutwood…" As the chums ride on they suddenly catch sight of the sea and a magnificent building set high on the cliff-tops...

As soon as the carriage arrives at the palace, Li-Poo comes hurrying across the courtyard to greet the friends. "Thank goodness you're here!" he gasps. "Things have been terrible! I didn't know what to do or where to turn!" "Whatever's wrong?" blinks Pong-Ping. "The Emperor!" quails Li-Poo. "Is he ill?" asks the Peke. "Worse!" gasps the courtier. "He's disappeared!" "Disappeared?" gasps Rupert in amazement. "Vanished!" nods the Mandarin. "I'm afraid His Excellency has been kidnapped!"

RUPERT HEARS WHAT HAPPENED

*"The scoundrels seized His Majesty
As we were walking by the sea..."*

*"They rowed off quickly - out of reach
And left me standing on the beach!"*

*"The kidnappers have been in touch
But their demands are far too much..."*

*"Black pearls!" gasps Pong-Ping. "That would be
Impossible! I quite agree!"*

"The Emperor and I went for a walk along the beach," explains Li-Poo. "It was the same route we always take, to admire the view. At first all was well but, as we rounded the headland, a gang of brigands suddenly appeared, waving swords and shouting threats. Before I could raise the alarm, they bundled His Majesty into a boat and rowed out to sea. There was a bigger boat waiting for them, a pirate junk I think. By the time the guards arrived they had sailed away, taking the Emperor with them..."

Continuing his tale of the Emperor's disappearance, Li-Poo produces a folded note. "The next morning, this arrived!" he declares. "It is a ransom demand from the kidnappers. See for yourselves and you will understand my dilemma..." Rupert unfolds the letter. He is about to hand it to Pong-Ping to translate when he suddenly blinks with surprise. "It's written in English!" he cries. "The kidnappers are demanding the Emperor's weight in pearls..." "Black pearls!" gasps Pong-Ping. "But that's impossible..."

*Li-Poo explains, "Black pearls are rare -
You can't just find them anywhere..."*

*"I've searched the whole Royal Treasury
And all we have are those you see!"*

*"Black pearls all come from this spot here,
Gathered by people who live near..."*

*"They've promised me a whole year's haul -
We'll go now, to collect them all!"*

"Black?" blinks Rupert when he hears the kidnappers' demand. "But I thought pearls were always silvery..." "Most are," nods Li-Poo, "But the rarest and most valuable are shiny black. Come with me and I'll show you what they're like..." To the pals' astonishment, the pearls are in a tall glass jar, guarded by two sentries from the Royal Guard. "These are all we have in the Royal Treasury!" sighs Li-Poo. "Extremely precious, but not enough to pay the Emperor's ransom..."

Turning to a map of China, Li-Poo tells Rupert and Pong-Ping why black pearls are so difficult to find... "The only oysters to produce them live off the coast of these islands," he declares. "Even then, most of the pearls they make are not black but the same colour as those found elsewhere. The Pearl Fishers of these islands are our only hope. I have sent word of the Emperor's disappearance and asked for all the pearls they can muster. A boat stands ready to take us there immediately..."

RUPERT SPOTS THE PEARL ISLANDS

The boat speeds off without delay,
"The islands are not far away..."

Before long, Rupert gives a cry.
"Look! There, between the sea and sky..."

The chums draw nearer. From their boat
They see a host of craft afloat...

Young boys are diving everywhere -
"Pearl Fishers!" Li-Poo tells the pair.

As soon as Li-Poo and the chums have climbed aboard, the motor boat speeds away from the Summer Palace, out to sea. "It is fortunate the Islands are not further away!" declares the Mandarin. "The Pearl Fishers are loyal subjects of His Majesty and have promised to find as many black pearls as they can. Even so, I have grave misgivings! The quantity demanded is unheard of. It would normally take years to find so many pearls." "Land ahoy!" calls Rupert. "I can see something on the horizon..."

As they draw nearer to the islands, Rupert can see a flotilla of little boats, bobbing about in the sea... "They're all Pearl Fishers!" gasps Pong-Ping. Each boat has baskets full of oysters, which teams of divers are busy bringing up from the sea bed. "Amazing!" blinks Rupert. "There must be hundreds of them..." "Certainly," nods Li-Poo. "All the islanders gather pearls. They start as divers, then work towards owning their own boat..."

RUPERT VOLUNTEERS TO HELP

The Fishers' Chief welcomes Li-Poo,
"We've been diving non-stop for you..."

"Black pearls are scarce, as well you know,
Our task is hard and very slow."

The Diver shows Li-Poo a jar -
"The few black pearls we've found so far..."

"While you stay here we'll try to find
What clues the pirates left behind!"

Putting ashore at the largest island, Li-Poo and the chums are greeted by the Divers' chief. "Welcome!" he calls. "We have been hard at work ever since your message. Every diver is gathering pearls for the Emperor's ransom. Their only thought is for his safe release..." "Thank you," says Li-Poo. "How is the search progressing?" "Slowly," admits the Chief. "For every black pearl there are a hundred ordinary ones and, for every pearl, a hundred oysters containing nothing at all!"

"This jar contains all the black pearls we have gathered so far," the diver tells Li-Poo. "The rest are ordinary pearls collected over the same period." "So few?" gasps Li-Poo. "It will take years to get enough!" "Perhaps we can help?" suggests Pong-Ping. "Rupert and I could return to the Palace and search for clues. If we knew where the Emperor has been taken, your soldiers might be able to set him free!" "Very well!" agrees Li-Poo. "Take a boat and return at once, but do be careful..."

RUPERT'S BOAT IS BECALMED

Pong-Ping and Rupert vow that they
Will find the pirates' hideaway...

"If Ming can scent the pirates' trail
He'll find them for us without fail..."

The boat's engine splutters and pops -
It slows suddenly and then stops!

"The fuel tank's empty!" blinks Pong-Ping.
"We're stranded! I can't do a thing!"

"I'm afraid they'll never collect enough black pearls to meet the ransom demand!" declares Pong-Ping as the pals set off towards the Summer Palace. "Finding where they've taken the Emperor is our only chance of defeating the kidnappers." "You're right," agrees Rupert. "But it won't be easy! Li-Poo said they took him away in a rowing boat to a pirate junk. It could be anywhere by now..." "Perhaps," nods Pong-Ping. "But there may still be a trail that Ming can follow..."

As Rupert and Pong-Ping make their way back towards the Summer Palace, the engine of their boat suddenly starts to splutter... "Something's wrong!" gasps the Peke. "We're losing speed!" He tries to adjust the controls but the motor will go no faster. To the pals' dismay it finally cuts out completely. "We must have run out of fuel!" blinks Pong-Ping. "What a thing to happen!" "We'll just have to drift with the tide!" says Rupert. "I hope we're not too far from land!"

RUPERT SEES MING CAPTURED

The pals drift helplessly afloat -
Till Rupert spots a distant boat...

"Hurrah! We're safe now," calls Pong-Ping.
"They'll come and help us. I'll send Ming."

A cannon roars as Ming flies by
And fires a net into the sky...

"Oh, no! They've captured Ming! But who
Can they be? It's the Pirate crew!"

Stranded in the little boat, with no idea where they are, Rupert and Pong-Ping look anxiously around for any sign of land... "I can't see anything," says Rupert, then, suddenly, he spots the sails of a ship on the horizon. "Saved!" laughs his friend delightedly. "Ming can fly over to them and raise the alarm. It's probably a merchant ship on its way in to port. I'm sure they won't mind giving us a tow..." Flapping his wings, the little dragon sets off across the sea towards the junk.

Rupert and Pong-Ping watch as Ming flies across the sea towards the distant ship. To their surprise, they hear a low boom, then see a sudden puff of smoke. "A cannon!" cries the Peke... Equally astonished by this unexpected turn of events, Ming finds himself trapped in a heavy net which flies through the air towards him. Flapping his wings angrily, he feels it tighten around him as the ship's crew haul on ropes. "The pirates!" gasps Pong-Ping. "First they caught the Emperor, now they've caught Ming!"

RUPERT AND PONG-PING ESCAPE

*The cannon booms again. "Look out!
It's us now!" Pong-Ping gives a shout.*

*"That's close!" gasps Rupert. "If we're hit
We'll have to try to swim for it!"*

*As cannon-balls sail through the air
Two turtles swim towards the pair...*

*"It isn't safe for you to stay -
Climb on our backs. We'll swim away."*

Still shocked by Ming's capture, the pals hear the pirates' cannon fire again... "They're aiming at us now!" calls Pong-Ping. "With a net?" blinks Rupert. "No!" cries his chum, crouching down as a cannon ball whizzes through the air. "We're too far away for that. They must have decided to sink us! That shot missed, thank goodness, but we're still a sitting target!" "What shall we do?" gasps Rupert. "If the boat goes down we'll have to try and swim to dry land..."

The terrified chums crouch lower and lower as a hail of cannon balls sails through the air towards them. Just as it seems certain they will sink, two enormous turtles appear, alerted by all the noise... "Pirates, eh?" says the first. "Hardly fair if you can't fire back! Just as well we came along..." "Climb on our backs!" the other turtle calls. "We'll take you to safety. You'll be far away by the time those ruffians find you've abandoned ship. Don't be nervous, just hold on tight!"

RUPERT LANDS ON AN ISLAND

The turtles swim off rapidly,
Away from the junk - out to sea...

"A little island!" Rupert blinks.
"We must be heading there," he thinks.

The pals land on a sandy beach -
"You should be safe here, out of reach!"

They take a path which Pong-Ping sees,
Winding its way between the trees...

The turtles start to swim away with Rupert and Pong-Ping perched on their backs. The pirates' cannon fires again but they are soon out of range and head steadily on, across the open sea. At first the chums have no idea where they are going, then the first turtle gives a sudden cry. "Land ahoy!" it calls. "An island!" blinks Rupert. "You'll be safe from pirates there." says the second turtle. "They'll never think to follow you, and if they do they'll live to regret it!"

When they reach the island, the turtles swim on to a sandy beach where the chums can climb ashore... "Stay out of sight until the danger has passed!"they warn. "The pirates may sail in this direction but you should be safely hidden by all the trees and ferns..." Thanking their rescuers, Rupert and Pong-Ping hurry off, under a canopy of leaves, with exotic flowers and fruit growing all round. "This way," says the Peke. "Towards the middle of the island. I think I can see a grassy path..."

RUPERT IS ARRESTED

The two chums cross the isle and then
Gaze out across the sea again...

A sudden voice calls out, "Who's there?"
Two monkey guards confront the pair.

"This island's private! You can't stay
Without permission! Come this way..."

A flight of steps leads underground
While lamps show where the pals are bound.

Following the path, the pals eventually come to another stretch of coast. "We've walked right across the island!" says Rupert. "It seems to be completely uninhabited." "Look!" calls Pong-Ping. "There are more little islands on the horizon..." To the chums' amazement they suddenly hear someone coming. "Who's there?" calls a voice. The pair spin round to see two fierce-looking monkeys, wearing pearl-studded helmets. "Strangers!" snaps their leader. "What are you doing on the Forbidden Isle?"

"Forbidden Isle?" blinks Rupert. "We thought nobody lived here..." "You were wrong!" says one of the monkey guards. "This island is private. Our leader permits no-one to land. Return to your boat at once." "We can't!" says Pong-Ping. "We came by turtle. They brought us here for safe-keeping..." "Friends of the Turtles!" says the second guard. "That makes a difference. Come with us! Our leader will decide what is to be done." Squeezing through a gap in the rocks they point to a steep flight of steps...

The chums approach a chamber where
A king sits in a massive chair...

"We've caught a pair who say they came
By turtle - an unlikely claim!"

"Our boat was fired on by a crew
Of pirates! They're kidnappers too..."

"The Emperor must be set free!
I'll send pearls from my Treasury..."

At the foot of the steps, the astounded pals find a narrow tunnel which leads to a rocky chamber hung with pearl-studded drapes. Before them sits a regal figure wearing an enormous turban... "Who is this?" he demands as the newcomers approach. "Visitors, Excellency!" shrugs the first guard. "They say they were brought here by turtles..." "Indeed?" blinks the island's ruler. "A rather far-fetched claim! Explain your presence, young Sirs. I don't take kindly to treasure-seekers..."

When Rupert explains how he and Pong-Ping were attacked by pirates, the ruler of the Forbidden Isle agrees that the turtles were right to bring them ashore... "A scourge of the seas!" he tuts. "I'm sure they're the same gang who have kidnapped the Emperor!" adds Rupert. "They've demanded his weight in black pearls..." "The Emperor!" gasps the little man. "But this is terrible! I'd no idea. Pearls are nothing compared with the safety of a fellow King. I must send the ransom at once!"

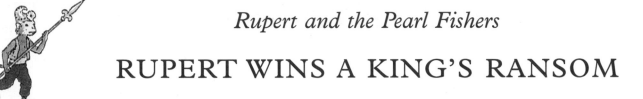

Rupert and the Pearl Fishers

RUPERT WINS A KING'S RANSOM

The guards are sent off at full speed –
"Get all the black pearls these two need!"

"This way!" the King says. "Follow me.
This tunnel leads down to the sea..."

They come to where a boat is moored,
With guards loading black pearls aboard...

"So many black pearls! I'm sure they
Match what the Emperor must weigh."

"Black pearls!" the monkeys' ruler commands. "Fill a boat with them at once. Tell the chief turtle we need him as well. A special mission. Hurry now, as quickly as you can..." To the chums' surprise, he leads the way out of the chamber and down a second flight of steps. "Shortest way to the sea!" he explains. "I'm sending a boat to the mainland. You can go too. Good job you landed here! Plenty of pearls in my Treasury. Never mind giving them to a good cause. Happy to oblige..."

Following the Pearl King, Rupert and Pong-Ping reach an underground cave with a hidden outlet to the sea. A cockleshell boat stands ready to leave, brimful of gleaming black pearls... "Our fastest turtle will tow you!" declares the King. "You can ride upon his back." "Amazing!" blinks Rupert. "It would take the Pearl Fishers years to gather all these..." "Us too!" nods the King. "But the Emperor's need is greater than mine. I only hope those rascally pirates keep their word!"

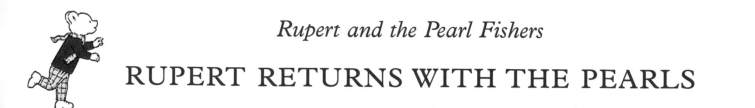

"Farewell!" the Pearl King calls. "Please let
Me know how things go! Don't forget..."

The two chums leave the isle and then
Head for the mainland once again.

"The Palace!" Rupert gives a cheer
As the turtle starts drawing near.

Li-Poo comes hurrying to see
What the pals' latest news can be...

As soon as the shell is full, Rupert and Pong-Ping climb carefully on to the turtle's back... "Farewell!" calls the Pearl King. "I look forward to hearing news of the Emperor. He is fortunate to have such friends..." "Thank you!" replies Pong-Ping. "We will deliver the pearls to His Majesty's Chamberlain straightaway..." The turtle swims off with the precious cargo safely stowed behind the chums. "To the Emperor's Summer Palace!" commands Pong-Ping. "As quickly as you can..."

As the turtle swims towards the mainland, Rupert and Pong-Ping spot the towers of the Summer Palace. "Well done!" cheers Rupert. "We're nearly there..." The chums' arrival causes quite a stir, with Li-Poo hurrying down to meet them. "Any luck?" he calls anxiously. "The ransom demand is impossible for us to meet in time. Unless we find the Pirates' ship, I fear His Excellency will remain their prisoner for many months..." "Don't worry!" calls Pong-Ping. We've come back with wonderful news!"

RUPERT PLANS A TRAP

"So many pearls! Now we can pay
The ransom demand straightaway!"

"No!" says the Chief Guard. "That won't do!
We need to catch the pirates too!"

"Wait!" Rupert says. "I know how we
Can stop the pirates! Come with me..."

When all is ready, late that night,
The pals watch, hidden, out of sight...

The old Mandarin can hardly believe his eyes when he sees the enormous shell full of black pearls... "The Emperor's ransom!" he gasps. "We'll be able pay it, after all!" "Pay?" growls the Chief of the Palace Guard. "We cannot simply hand such a fortune to pirates. We must search the seas for their boat. They must be punished for daring to kidnap the Emperor!" "You're right," says Rupert. "But paying the ransom will help us catch them. Listen carefully and I'll tell you what to do..."

When Li-Poo and the Chief Guard hear Rupert's plan, they soon agree to do as he suggests... "The Emperor's safety must come first!" declares Li-Poo. "I too would like the rascals punished but if we must hand over the ransom I am prepared to see it go..." "Good," nods Rupert. "The first thing we'll need are some big pots to hold the pearls. If we stand them on the beach, the kidnappers will be able to see their demands have been met. We'll stay out of sight and wait for their boat to come..."

RUPERT SEES THE PIRATES' LEADER

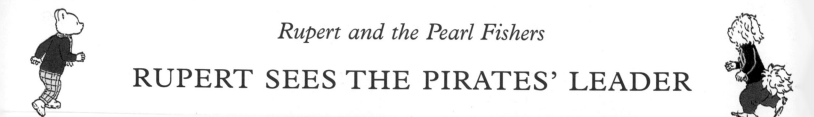

*"Look, Pong-Ping! It's the junk we saw –
With red sails. The pirates, I'm sure..."*

*"The Emperor!" cries Li-Poo. "We
Must hope these bandits set him free!"*

*The watching chums gasp with surprise
To see someone they recognise...*

*"Sir Humphrey Pumphrey! He must be
Behind the whole plot! Goodness me!"*

Hidden behind a rock, the chums look out to sea for signs of the pirates. For a long time nothing happens, then Rupert suddenly spots a ship with red sails... "It's them!" he whispers. "The same junk that fired at us!" Moments later, a ferocious looking band disembarks and marches along the shore towards the enormous pots. "The Emperor!" gasps Li-Poo. "The pirates have His Majesty with them. So long as he is returned safely, the pearls will be a small price to pay..."

As the pirates get nearer, Rupert gives a sudden cry of surprise. "Humphrey Pumphrey!" he blinks. "He's got Ming on a lead!" gasps Pong-Ping. "Who is this you speak of?" asks Li-Poo. "A member of the pirate crew?" "So it seems!" nods Rupert. "Sir Humphrey must be their boss! He's always trying to catch rare animals, but I didn't know he'd turn to kidnapping people! I suppose it's the lure of black pearls. He must have found out how rare they are, then thought up a plan to get some..."

RUPERT ALERTS THE GUARDS

Sir Humphrey and the pirates beam.
"We'll all be rich! It's like a dream!"

"You're free to go, Your Majesty,
I always keep my word, you see..."

"The Emperor!" calls Rupert. "How
Glad I am that you're back safe now!"

"A trap!" Sir Humphrey starts to cry
As soldiers make the black pearls fly...

From their hiding place behind the rocks, Rupert and Pong-Ping watch Sir Humphrey Pumphrey examining a pot full of black pearls... "Splendid!" he cries. "An Emperor's ransom! I'll be rich for the rest of my life! You too!" he tells the pirates' chief. "I couldn't have carried this off without your help..." As the pirates gloat over their prize, Pumphrey orders them to untie the Emperor then tells him he's free to leave. "A fair exchange!" he smiles. "I like to keep my word..."

As he walks away from Sir Humphrey and the pirates, the Emperor is amazed to see Rupert and Pong-Ping... "Your Majesty!" calls Rupert. "I'm so glad you are safe and sound!" The moment he speaks, a cry of dismay goes up from the pirates. Fierce-looking guards spring from each of the pots, scattering pearls into the air. "Tricked!" gasps Sir Humphrey. "It's a trap..." "Exactly!" says the soldiers' chief. "The Emperor's enemies have been vanquished! Long live His Excellency!"

RUPERT IS GIVEN A ROYAL GIFT

Stern guards surround the pirate crew -
"The Emperor will deal with you!"

"Another captive's free now - Ming!"
The dragon runs to greet Pong-Ping.

The Emperor tells Rupert how
He'd like to give him a gift now...

He smiles and hands the Nutwood pair
A string of pearls for Mrs. Bear!

"Hurrah!" cheers Pong-Ping as Sir Humphrey and the pirates are rounded up. "Rupert's plan worked..." "Wonderful!" says Li-Poo. "His Majesty is safe and the kidnappers have been brought to Justice!" "Take them away!" booms the Emperor. "The miscreants shall be my prisoners now!" "Ming's free too!" laughs Pong-Ping as the little dragon bounds towards him. "To think of Sir Humphrey keeping him in his private zoo! My pet's worth more to me than all the pearls in China..."

When he hears how Rupert and Pong-Ping managed to outwit the pirates, the Emperor is so overjoyed that he insists on making them a presentation from the Royal Treasury. "A string of fine pearls for Mrs. Bear!" he smiles. "To remind you of your adventure and also to express my thanks to her resourceful son!" "Goodness!" gasps Rupert as he takes the necklace. "Won't Mum be surprised! I can hardly wait to get back to Nutwood and tell her the whole story..."

RUPERT
and the
Nut Hatch

John Harrold.

RUPERT AND BILL LOOK FOR CONKERS

This Autumn Bill and Rupert plan
To find some conkers, if they can...

"That's very strange! There's nothing here -
It's where we find them every year..."

As Rupert searches, Bill sees two
More Nutwood chums come into view.

"Hello!" calls Algy. "All we've found
Are just these, lying on the ground."

It is autumn in Nutwood. The leaves of the trees have started to turn and Rupert and Bill are up on the common, looking for conkers... "Have you found any yet?" asks Bill. "None!" says Rupert. "All I can see are leaves..." "Me too!" nods his pal. "I suppose somebody must have beaten us to it!" "Probably Freddy and Ferdy!" laughs Rupert. "I expect they came out early and gathered all they could find. Even so, it does seem odd. I can't even see any empty husks..."

Rupert and Bill try looking under all their favourite trees but they can't find a single conker. They are still searching when Bill spots two familiar figures, strolling across the common... "Hello!" calls Algy Pug. "Looking for conkers? You'll be lucky to find any up here! Willie and I have tried everywhere we can think of and all we've found are these!" "Two!" blinks Rupert. "There are normally plenty for everyone. I wonder why they're suddenly so difficult to find?"

The pals are both surprised to see
Old Gaffer Jarge beneath a tree...

"Sweet chestnuts are my favourite kind -
But it seems there are none to find!"

The chums try every tree they know -
But still don't have a thing to show...

"The squirrels were complaining too -
They've had a fruitless search, like you!"

Deciding to continue with their search, Rupert and Bill are surprised to come across Gaffer Jarge... "I didn't know you played conkers!" smiles Rupert. "Conkers?" scoffs the old man. "'Tain't conkers I'm after! They're horse chestnuts. Sweet chestnuts are what I want. For roasting on the fire. Delicious, they are! Different husks to conkers. More prickles. Pale green. I'd show you one, if I could. Haven't found any all morning! I can't think what's happened to them all..."

Leaving Gaffer Jarge to look for sweet chestnuts, Rupert and Bill continue on their way but still don't have any luck... "I don't believe it!" sighs Bill. "We haven't found a single conker!" "You're not the only ones to complain," calls a nearby voice. "Horace!" blinks Rupert. "Shouldn't you be hibernating by now?" "Nearly time!" smiles the hedgehog. "As soon as the weather turns cold. The squirrels have been searching too, you know! Acorns, beech-nuts, they're all in short supply!"

RUPERT INVESTIGATES

"I've never known nuts disappear
Like this in any other year!"

A squirrel scampers down to tell
How she's heard something odd as well...

She bounds ahead from tree to tree -
"I'll lead the way! Just follow me!"

"That's it!" she cries. The chums can hear
A droning sound from somewhere near...

"It's strange!" yawns Horace. "I've never known conkers disappear like this! Squirrels hoard acorns, but they wouldn't take horse chestnuts." "Certainly not!" calls a voice. "They taste horrible!" Looking up, the pals see a squirrel peering from a nearby branch. "Horace!" she cries. "I heard a strange noise in the forest! It might be the creature that's taking all the nuts..." "I'm afraid I'm too sleepy to be much help," says the hedgehog. "Why don't you show these two what you've found..."

Leaping from tree to tree, the squirrel leads Rupert and Bill into the forest... "It's kind of you to help!" she says. "We woodland creatures need a store of acorns and beech-nuts to survive the winter! If they keep disappearing like this there won't be enough to go round." As they follow their guide, the chums suddenly hear a strange droning sound. "That's it!" gasps the squirrel. "It certainly sounds strange," blinks Rupert. "Like...like someone using a vacuum cleaner!"

RUPERT SPOTS SOME ELVES

The two chums can't believe their eyes -
"It's Autumn Elves! What a surprise."

They gather conkers from the ground,
Collecting every one they've found...

Rupert and Bill keep out of view,
Watching to see what the Elves do.

The chums are both surprised to see
A hatch cut in a hollow tree...

As the chums creep forward, they are amazed to see two of Nutwood's Autumn Elves... "They are using some sort of vacuum cleaner!" blinks Bill. "Sucking up conkers!" gasps Rupert. "No wonder we couldn't find any..." The pair stand staring in astonishment as each Elf fills the basket on his back with fallen chestnuts. "Husks and all!" whispers Bill. "What do you suppose they're up to? Why are the Elves hoovering up conkers? I thought they gathered nuts and seeds by hand..."

Remembering how Nutwood's Elves like to go about their work secretly, Rupert and Bill keep out of sight as the pair walk off with their baskets full to the brim... "What now?" whispers Bill. "They've stopped by a old oak..." As the chums look on, they see the Elves open a hidden door. "It's hollow!" says Rupert. "Perhaps they're going to climb inside?" To his surprise, the Elves remove their baskets and tip them out in a cascade of husks and shiny conkers. "How odd!" he murmurs.

RUPERT SLIDES DOWN A CHUTE

The Elves empty their baskets then
Close up the secret hatch again...

The pals approach the secret store.
"Let's try to open up the door!"

The hatch swings open, "What's inside?"
"A chute! It's like a metal slide..."

As Bill leans forward, suddenly,
The pals fall down, into the tree!

As soon as the Elves have emptied their baskets, they shut the hatch and head off across the common, towards another stand of trees... "What do you make of that?" asks Bill. "It must be some sort of secret store!" "I wonder?" says Rupert. "The door looked easy enough to open. I don't suppose they'd mind if we took a peek..." "Go on!" urges Bill. "Just a check, to see how many they've got. If all the Elves have been out gathering there won't be a conker left in the whole of Nutwood!"

Pulling open the hatch in the hollow tree, Rupert finds a smooth metal chute which juts over a deep, dark pit... "Gosh!" blinks Bill. "It's bigger than I thought! I wonder how far down it goes?" As his chum leans forward for a better view, Rupert suddenly feels the chute move, sending him sprawling into the darkness. "Help!" cries Bill. "The door's closing behind us!" Before he can stop, he finds himself sliding down after Rupert, towards the base of the hollow tree...

RUPERT MEETS THE CHIEF ELF

The pair end up deep underground,
Where startled Elves are gathered round...

The Elves crowd round and all begin
To ask the pals how they got in.

Their Chief appears. "What's this? Who's there?"
He calls out as he spots the pair.

"No harm done!" smiles the Chief. "Now you're
Down here, I'll take you on a tour..."

As they go sliding down the chute, Rupert and Bill expect to reach the bottom almost immediately. Instead, they find themselves falling down a long, dark tunnel, which seems to go deep underground... To their utter amazement, they finally emerge to a glow of bright lights, landing in huge tub of conkers, which are being sorted by three more Autumn Elves... "What? Who? How?" stammers their leader, looking even more startled than the Nutwood chums...

"I'm sorry!" says Rupert. "We just couldn't resist looking inside the hollow tree..." "You opened our hatch?" scowls one of the sorters. "Only Elves are allowed to do that! Not Nutwooders, like you..." "Nutwooders?" calls a stern voice. "What are they doing here?" The Chief Elf demands to hear Rupert's story... "Highly irregular!" he tuts. "But I can't really blame you for being curious..." To the pals' delight, the Chief breaks into a broad smile. "Now you're here, I'll show you what happens next!"

RUPERT IS GIVEN A GUIDED TOUR

*"Down here we sort the nuts we find -
Sweet chestnuts, conkers, every kind..."*

*The pals are taken to be shown
How all the seeds and nuts are grown.*

*"Each conker that we plant has got
Some growing mixture in its pot..."*

*"The little seedlings soon come out -
Bright light and tonic helps them sprout."*

Forgiven by the Elves, Rupert and Bill find themselves being given a conducted tour by the Chief... "You've seen how the nuts are gathered," he says. "And here you see them being sorted. Conkers in one box, sweet chestnuts in another. Beech nuts, acorns, they all need sorting out, you know. When the boxes are full we take them through to the Arboretum." "Arboretum?" blinks Rupert. "Tree nursery," smiles the Chief. "This is just the beginning. Growing trees is a lengthy business..."

From the sorting chamber, Rupert and Bill are taken to another room, where Elves are busy planting conkers and acorns in individual flowerpots..."Amazing!" blinks Rupert. "I wonder if I could grow a tree like that?" "Of course!" says the Elf. "You'd have to wait a bit longer than us, though. We use a special growing mixture to speed things up a bit..." "It's just like a factory!" gasps Bill. "What happens next?" "Seedlings!" says the Elf. "They're next door..."

RUPERT SEES THE ARBORETUM

*"These saplings look like little trees -
An oak will grow from each of these!"*

*"This way!" the Chief calls. "Follow me!
There's one more stage for you to see..."*

*"The trees spend one year here, then they
Are moved again, to where they'll stay."*

*"Our Arboretum lets us grow
New trees where we think they should go..."*

"This way!" calls the Chief Elf. "These pots are full of seedlings. We grow them under extra bright lights and water them with tree tonic. You can see for yourselves how quickly they turn into little saplings..." "They're miniature trees now!" laughs Bill. "Oaks by the look of it." "That's right!" nods the Chief. "You can always tell by the shape of the leaves. I always make a final inspection, just in case any have been muddled up. These are nearly ready to be transferred outside..."

Following the Chief Elf, the chums reach a small, circular door... "We're back on the common!" blinks Bill. "The edge of it," nods the Chief. "This is where we harden off new trees. A season here in the open air and they're ready to be moved to their final homes..." "Remarkable!" says Rupert. "I thought new trees just grew wherever acorns or conkers fell to earth..." "Forest management!" beams the Chief Elf. "This way we can control exactly what goes on..."

"But what about the nuts and seeds
That every woodland creature needs?"

"You two were quite right to protest -
We'll stop now and leave all the rest!"

The Chief says he will make amends
And give some chestnuts to the friends...

The Elves bring two big baskets out -
"Sweet chestnuts and conkers!" they shout.

"It sounds wonderful," says Rupert. "But what about all the woodland creatures? Your Elves have been so good at gathering nuts that there's none left for anyone else!" "Oh, dear!" sighs the Chief. "I suppose you're right! I never thought of anyone else..." "Your Arboretum's still a good idea," says Rupert. "You just need to leave more behind..." The Elf looks thoughtful, then breaks into a broad smile. "We will!" he cries. "We'll stop collecting nuts for this year and leave all the rest where they fall..."

"Not only will we stop collecting," says the Chief Elf. "But our store of nuts will be used to make good any harm we've done!" "You mean you'll give some back?" blinks Bill. "Exactly!" nods the Chief. "Acorns for the squirrels and conkers for you! Perhaps you'd like some sweet chestnuts too?" "Yes, please!" laughs Rupert. "I know somebody in Nutwood who'd be very glad of those..." In next to no time, two Elves appear with baskets filled to the brim. "One of each!" they smile.

RUPERT RETURNS WITH CHESTNUTS

*"Goodbye!" the Elves call. "Next year we
Will leave nuts underneath each tree..."*

*The chums show Gaffer Jarge their haul -
"We've got some chestnuts, after all!"*

*"Well done, you two! I'll roast the lot!
They taste delicious when they're hot..."*

*"Hey! You two! Look what we've got here!
Enough conkers to last the year..."*

"Thanks for your warning!" calls the Chief Elf as the chums wave farewell. "Next year, we'll go back to gathering nuts by hand!" Walking back across the common, the pals spot Gaffer Jarge, still searching under a spreading tree... "Come on!" laughs Rupert. "Let's show him what we've got!" "Hello, young 'uns!" says Gaffer Jarge. "What's that in those baskets?" "Chestnuts!" beams Rupert. "One's for you, while the other is for us to share..."

"Chestnuts?" blinks the old man. "But I've been looking for those all morning..." "We did have a bit of help," admits Bill. "Someone we met had been collecting too..." "Good for them!" smiles Gaffer. "There's enough chestnuts here for the whole of Nutwood..." Leaving Gaffer Jarge with his unexpected prize, Rupert and Bill go off in search of their chums, who are just as pleased to see their haul... "Marvellous!" says Algy. "Now we can all play at conkers."

THE END

These two pictures look identical, but there are ten differences between them. Can you spot them all? *Answers on page 109*

Rupert's Crossword Puzzle

See if you can complete this crossword. Most of the answers can be found
in stories from this year's annual . . .

ACROSS

1. Demanded by kidnappers (6)
5. Magic request (4)
6. Rupert's smallest chum (6,5)
8. Another of Rupert's chums- A.P. (4,3)
9. Nutwood's hedgehog (6)
11. A greedy pig (5)
13. Single number (3)
16. Mischievous Nutwood brothers (3,5)
18. Precious sphere- from 32 across (5)
21. Sea King (7)
24. Bushy-tailed woodland creature (8)
27. Finish/stop (3)
28. Chinese boat with distinctive sail (4)
29. Rupert's elephant friend (6)
32. Shell-fish, produces 18 across (6)
34. Not in (3)
37. Nutwood visitor, cousin of 3 down (3)
38. Eastern country, visited by Rupert (5)
40. Conjurer's daughter (9)
41. Consume/devour (3)
42. Wise bird (3)
43. Get away (6)
47. Shout (4)
48. Ancient (3)
50. Get bigger (4)
51. Not shut (4)
53. Halt (4)
54. Sea-faring thief (6)

DOWN

1. Wet, falls from the sky (4)
2. Frozen version of 1 down (4)
3. Badger, Rupert's best friend (4)
4. Pong-Ping's pet dragon (4)
7. Wise old man (4,2,2)
9. Another name for a conker (5,8)
10. Nutwood's oldest inhabitant (6,5)
12. Otter who lives at Nutwood Manor (8)
14. Opposite of full (5)
15. Colour of fish which eats blue seaweed (4)
17. Frozen water (3)
19. Sixth month of the year (4)
20. Leader of Autumn Elves (5)
22. Daughter of a king (8)
23. Last month of the year (8)
25. Beachcomber (3)
26. Rupert's guinea-pig chum (7)
30. Twice (6)
31. Festival held in 23 down (9)
33. Rupert's favourite seaside resort (5,3)
35. Large sea-creature, has a shell (6)
36. Competition- won by the fastest (4)
39. Rupert's village (7)
44. Worn by 22 down, or her parents (5)
45. Young Royal servant (4)
46. Permit (5)
49. Final (4)
52. Seed- apple, orange or lemon (3)

How carefully can you colour these two pictures?

A PAGE TO COLOUR

Whose Hat?

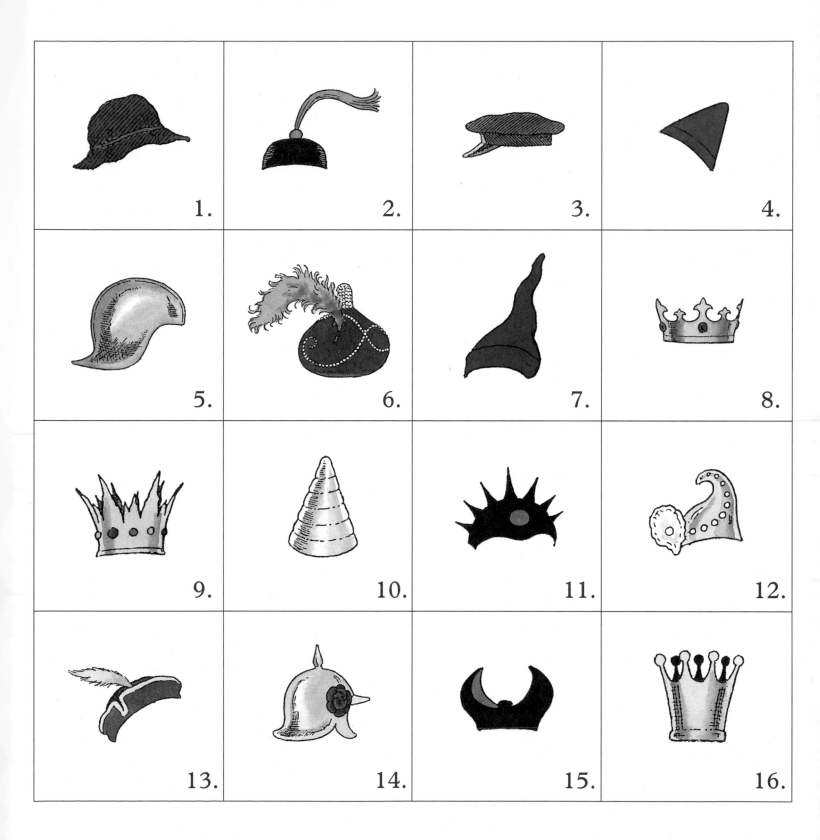

Each of the hats shown above belongs to a character you have met in this year's Rupert Annual.
Can you work out who owns each one? *Answers on page 109*

RUPERT and

*One morning, after Christmas Day,
Rupert decides to go and play...*

Christmas Day has been and gone in Nutwood and Rupert and his parents have enjoyed a wonderful break... "I think I'll go up to the common to see if I can find any chums to play with," says Rupert. "Good idea," smiles Mrs. Bear. "You can invite them back for some mince pies if you like!" To Rupert's delight, several of his pals have had the same idea. Before long, they are all happily playing football together, each taking a turn in goal...

John Harrold

the Christmas Box

*The chums play football - everyone
Joins in and all enjoy the fun.*

*"I'll see you later!" Rupert cries.
"Come round and have some hot mince pies!"*

When the game ends, Rupert invites his pals to drop by later. "Thanks!" says Bill. "That would be great. You can show me your presents. I'd better go and let my parents know first. Perhaps you can come and visit us tomorrow..." When Rupert gets home, he is surprised to see an unopened parcel standing all alone, under the Christmas tree. "That's odd!" he blinks. "I'm sure we opened everything on Christmas Day. I don't remember any gifts being left behind..."

*He arrives home, surprised to find
A present that's been left behind...*

RUPERT HAS AN EXTRA PRESENT

*"A box!" says Rupert. "Somebody
Has sent it to us specially."*

*"How odd!" blinks Mrs. Bear. "I'm sure
I didn't see it there before..."*

*"Who can it be from? We'll soon know -
As soon as I untie the bow..."*

*As Rupert watches, Mr. Bear
Exclaims, "Bless me! There's nothing there!"*

Picking up the mystery gift, Rupert finds that it is a brightly painted box, with a ribbon tied round it... "Perhaps somebody delivered it while I was out?" he thinks. "I wonder if Mum and Dad know what's inside?" When Rupert shows the box to his parents, they are just as surprised to see it as he was... "How very strange!" says Mrs. Bear. "We haven't had any callers all morning." "The Postman hasn't been either!" blinks Rupert's father. "I wonder who it's from?"

"I suppose we must have just missed this on Christmas Day!" says Rupert's father as he unties the ribbon round the mysterious box. "If it was mixed up with all the others, it might have got pushed behind the tree..." "Perhaps," says Mrs. Bear. "But I'm sure I haven't seen it before!" Rupert looks on expectantly as his father releases a catch and opens the box's hinged lid. "Bless me!" he blinks. "This is stranger than ever! It's completely empty. There's nothing inside at all..."

RUPERT'S PAL OPENS THE BOX

"It's very strange! Perhaps someone
Just thought they'd play a joke, for fun…"

"Hello, Bill! Come inside and see
What we found, underneath our tree."

"Whoever sent it left no name -
Guess what's inside! Let's play a game…"

"A toy!" laughs Bill as Rupert cries
"Impossible!" and rubs his eyes.

Rupert and his parents are completely mystified by the empty box… "What a strange thing to send anyone for Christmas!" he thinks. "I wonder if there's meant to be anything inside, or if someone's just playing a joke?" He is still looking at the box when Bill arrives. "You didn't send me a wooden box tied up with a ribbon, did you?" asks Rupert. "Me?" blinks Bill. "No, why?" "Come and see!" says Rupert. "We've had a strange delivery and nobody knows who it's from…"

Without saying another word, Rupert leads his chum in to see the strange box… "What do you make of it?" he asks. "Looks like a Jack-in-the-Box to me," says Bill. "Don't say you haven't opened it yet? How could you resist?" "Have a look inside," urges Rupert. "Go on, tell me what you see…" Releasing the catch, Bill opens the lid and smiles. "Very nice!" he laughs. "But why all the mystery?" "It…it is a Jack-in-the-Box!" blinks Rupert. "But that's impossible!"

RUPERT IS ASTONISHED

"The box was empty, Bill, I swear!
We looked inside - nothing was there..."

Before Rupert says any more,
Another chum knocks at the door.

"Hello Podgy! Let's see if you
Can guess what's inside this box too..."

"Toffees!" smiles Podgy. "What a treat!
I do like presents you can eat!"

"What's so strange about a Jack-in-the-Box?" asks Bill. "Nothing," blinks Rupert. "It's just that it wasn't there last time I looked! When the box arrived it was completely empty..." "Perhaps it has a secret compartment?" suggests Bill. "Close the lid and see what happens if you open it again..." The chums are just about to release the catch when Mrs. Bear appears with another Christmas visitor. "Hello!" says Podgy. "I came as soon as I could. I hope I'm not too late for the mince pies..."

"Never mind mince pies!" says Rupert. "What do you think is inside this box, Podgy? It's a mystery present that suddenly appeared under our tree..." "It looks like a box of sweets to me!" smiles Podgy. "Toffees!" he laughs as Rupert releases the catch. "They're my favourites! It's full to the brim. What a marvellous Christmas treat! I expect it's from one of your uncles. Uncle Bruno often sends presents. Perhaps it's from him? The label's probably fallen off in the post..."

RUPERT MAKES A WISH

"Toffees!" blinks Bill. "It can't be true!
Now I'm as mystified as you..."

"It must be magic!" Rupert beams.
"The box gives what you want, it seems..."

"I'll ask for something now. I know!
I wish that we could have some snow..."

As Rupert peers in, he can feel
Cold snowflakes on his face... "They're real!"

"Toffees!" gasps Bill. "Where have they come from? I don't understand..." "Neither do I!" blinks Mrs. Bear. "I thought the box was empty!" "It was," says Rupert. "The first time we looked there was nothing there. Then there was a Jack-in-the-box, now it's full of sweets! I wonder? Let's close the lid and see what happens next." "What do you think's going on?" asks Bill. "Magic!" smiles Rupert. "I think the box grants wishes. Everyone who opens it gets something different..."

"A wishing-box!" blinks Bill. "What are you going to ask it for?" "I don't know," says Rupert. "The only thing I'd really like is some snow to go sledging. I don't suppose the box can grant wishes like that..." Releasing the catch, he slowly opens the lid then peers inside. To Rupert's astonishment, a cold wind blows into his face, followed by flakes of snow which swirl into the room in a miniature blizzard... "I don't believe it!" cries Bill. "It's exactly what you asked for!"

RUPERT TAKES THE BOX OUTSIDE

"Quick, Rupert! Take that box of yours
And put it somewhere safe, outdoors…"

"What's that?" blinks Mr. Bear. "Oh, dear!
"How did a snowstorm get in here?"

The three chums run outside. "Now where?
The common! We can leave it there…"

The box keeps sending out more snow
Until a blizzard starts to blow!

"It's snowing indoors!" cries Mrs. Bear. "Rupert! Do something! Take that thing outside…" Seizing the box, Rupert runs from the room, while Bill hurries ahead of him to open the front door. The pair dash past an astonished Mr. Bear, who clearly can't believe his eyes. "It's snow!" cries Podgy. "Real snow! I'd rather have more toffees myself but you have to admit it's spectacular!" "Snow?" gasps Rupert's father. "But what's it doing in here? It's not even snowing outside…"

Clutching the wishing-box tightly, Rupert runs away from his house and up on to Nutwood common… "What now?" calls Bill as he and Podgy follow closely behind. "We'll leave it up here!" decides Rupert. "The snow won't bother anyone and we might even get a patch to play in…" "Good idea!" laughs Podgy. "It's still swirling up like a blizzard. I wonder if it will go on for long?" "Who knows?" shrugs Rupert. "The box seems to work by magic. I suppose it will just keep snowing until we've had enough…"

RUPERT SEES THICK SNOW

The three friends watch delightedly –
Then hurry home in time for tea…

"Well done!" says Mrs. Bear. "That box
Had far too many tricks and shocks!"

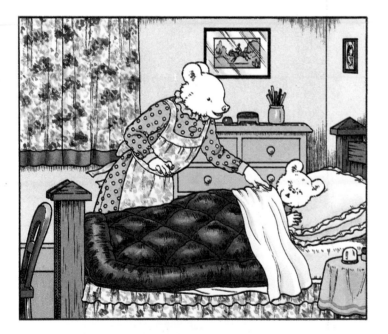

Next morning, Rupert wakes to find
The box has left his wish behind…

"The whole of Nutwood's covered in
Thick snow!" calls Rupert with a grin.

As the pals stand watching the box, it sends out more and more snow, till a great cloud hangs over Nutwood common. "Fantastic!" cheers Bill. "If it settles we can go sledging after all!" "Tomorrow will tell!" says Podgy."We'd better go home now, before it gets dark!" "See you tomorrow," calls Rupert. "I'll keep my fingers crossed!" When he gets home, Mrs. Bear has almost finished clearing up after the unexpected snowstorm. "Well done!" she tells Rupert. "We can't have blizzards in the house!"

The next morning, Mrs. Bear comes in to wake Rupert early with some surprising news… "Just wait until you look outside!" she says. "It looks as though that box of yours has covered the whole of Nutwood!" Jumping out of bed, Rupert hurries over to the window and gazes out on a thick, crisp coat of snow. "Wonderful!" he laughs. "It's just what I wanted. Now the box has granted my wish too. I'll be able to go out with the others and play in the snow all day!"

RUPERT PLAYS WITH HIS CHUMS

*"Look out!" laughs Bill as Rupert comes
Across the snow to join his chums...*

*The pals throw snowballs. Everyone
Joins in and shares the winter fun.*

*"The box!" says Bill. "Let's go and see
What the next wish it grants will be..."*

*"Look, there!" blinks Rupert. "This is weird!
The magic box has disappeared!"*

When Rupert reaches the common he finds his chums have all come to play in the snow... "Isn't this wonderful?" calls Bill. "It's just what we need!" The pals are soon having a snowball fight, with Podgy and Willie taking on the others. "Bull's eye!" laughs Podgy as he catches Algy. "My turn now!" calls Rupert. "Look out, Willie!" When they have had enough of snowballs the friends take turns on Algy's sledge, which speeds over the freshly fallen snow all the way to the bottom of the hill...

Rupert and his friends enjoy playing in the snow so much that they nearly forget all about the magic box... "I wonder if it will grant any more wishes?" says Bill. "We've all had a turn, but Willie and Algy might like to try their luck." The pals start looking for the high rock where Rupert stood the box. "Up there!" he cries. "I'm sure that's where we left it." "You're right," blinks Bill. "But there's nothing there now. The box has disappeared! I wonder where it's gone?"

RUPERT FOLLOWS A TRAIL

"Fresh footprints! Look, I've found a clue!
Someone's taken the box, but who?"

"This way!" says Rupert. "We'll soon find
The thieves. They've left a trail behind!"

"It's Farmer Brown's hut! Someone's there!
Two sets of footprints. It's a pair…"

"There's someone groaning!" Rupert blinks.
"They don't sound very well!" he thinks.

The chums are still puzzling over the disappearance of the magic box when Willie Mouse spots a trail of footprints in the snow… "Two people!" he calls. "They must have found the box and carried it off." "You might be right," nods Rupert. "I can see two sets of prints. They seem to lead along this way and over the brow of that hill…" "Fresh this morning!" says Podgy as the chums follow the trail. "Whoever made them must have been here early, just before we arrived…"

Rupert and his pals follow the trail of footprints across the common until they reach an old shed by the side of a copse. "Farmer Brown's shelter!" says Bill. "He sometimes uses it to store things. You don't suppose he's the one who's taken the box, do you?" "No," whispers Rupert. "There are two sets of footprints, side by side…" "Who can it be?" asks his chum as the pair tie-toe forward. "Listen!" says Rupert suddenly. "I can hear someone groaning. They don't sound very happy…."

RUPERT FINDS THE FOX TWINS

"The Fox brothers! I might have known!"
But what has made them wail and groan?

"It started with a box we found
Left empty, lying on the ground..."

"I took the box, then heard it make
A sound each time I gave a shake..."

"The empty box was full, somehow,
Of chocolate decorations now!"

"Freddy and Ferdy!" cries Rupert as the chums peer inside the shed. The Fox brothers are sitting near the open box, surrounded by brightly-coloured pieces of foil... "Er, hello, Rupert," says Freddy. "You're too late for a chocolate decoration, I'm afraid. We've just finished the last one." "I wish we hadn't!" groans Ferdy. "I never want to see another as long as I live!" "Do you know who the box belongs to?" asks his brother. "We found it out in the snow and decided to keep it..."

"The box was empty when we found it!" says Freddy. "I thought it might be useful for keeping things in but then, as we were on our way home, it suddenly started to rattle..." "We opened the lid and found it was full of chocolate Christmas tree decorations!" adds Ferdy. "Just what we wanted, as all ours were finished by Christmas Day..." "They tasted delicious!" says his brother. "I still don't know where they came from, but it was just like having someone grant a wish..."

RUPERT TAKES THE BOX HOME

"We can't eat any more today!
You'd better take the box away..."

"Poor things! They got their wish but still
Just ended up by feeling ill!"

"I'll take the box back home with me
And store it somewhere properly..."

But Mrs. Bear is horrified -
"No, Rupert! Take that box outside!"

At first, Rupert thinks the Fox brothers mean to keep the magic box but, to his surprise, they are quite happy to give it away... "No more chocolates for us!" groans Freddy. "I don't even want to open the lid and see if there are any more! You keep the box, Rupert. I'm going home for a lie down..." "Me too!" says Ferdy. "See you later, everyone." "Poor things!" says Rupert as the pair stagger off. "They did get a wish but it looks as though they'd have been better off without it!"

Glad to have recovered the box, Rupert tells the others he'll take it home with him for safe-keeping. "Good idea!" calls Bill. "We can try making another wish tomorrow!" When Rupert carries his prize into the house, Mrs. Bear is far less pleased to see it... "Not in here!" she cries. "I don't want any more showers of indoor snow! Put that box in the garden shed if you want to keep it. Goodness knows what it will come up with next! We'll store it outside where it can't do any harm..."

RUPERT'S MOTHER MAKES A WISH

"Somebody sent the box, but who?"
Says Mrs. Bear. "I wish we knew..."

The lid flies open. Smoke pours out
And coloured stars swirl all about...

"Look!" Rupert calls as the smoke clears -
His friend, The Sage of Um, appears.

"A spell I made went badly wrong -
I've been trapped inside all along!"

Rupert and his mother go out to the garden shed. While he unlocks the door, Mrs. Bear looks thoughtfully at the box. "I wish we knew who its owner was..." she murmurs. As she speaks, the lid flies open with a puff of coloured smoke. Stars swirl all around the astonished pair. "More tricks!" wails Rupert's mother. "I might have known something like this would happen!" To Rupert's amazement, the clearing smoke reveals a shadowy figure - who seems almost as surprised as the startled onlookers...

"The Sage of Um!" cries Rupert as he recognises the unexpected visitor. "Oh, dear!" blinks Mrs. Bear. "His foot's stuck in the box..." "Don't worry!" smiles the Sage. "There's no need for alarm. I have been stuck for a week or so, but your final wish has just set me free..." "Stuck inside the box?" asks Rupert as he helps his old friend up. "Exactly!" says the Sage. "A spell that went wrong, I'm afraid. The box was only meant to contain your Christmas presents..."

RUPERT GETS SOME SKIS

"*I muddled up the Sending Spell
And sent myself along as well!*"

"*I know it's late, but in here too
Are presents that I've brought for you...*"

"*I wonder what it is I've got?
There's something here. I can't see what...*"

The box has one last big surprise -
"*A pair of skis! Look!*" *Rupert cries.*

"I thought it would be fun to fill a box with presents for Nutwood," explains the Sage. "It was meant to arrive on Christmas Day. Everything was fine until I tried out the Sending Spell... I'm afraid I got the last verse muddled and sent myself as well!" "Goodness!" blinks Rupert's mother. "So you spent the whole holiday trapped inside..." "Indeed!" nods the Sage. "Still, better late than never! Your presents are in here too, you know. Open the lid and help yourselves..."

As the Sage of Um holds the box, Rupert reaches inside and feels for a parcel. "It's just like the Lucky Dip at Nutwood's Summer Fair!" he smiles. "Catch hold and pull!" laughs his friend. To Rupert's amazement, he finds himself holding a set of skis, all tied together with a bright red ribbon..." "I don't believe it!" blinks Mrs. Bear. "How did they fit into that little box?" "Magic!" beams the Sage. "I hope you like them, Rupert. Just the thing for a snowy, white Christmas..."

RUPERT'S FRIEND SAYS GOODBYE

*It's Mrs. Bear's turn. "Mitts! How nice!
They're perfect for the snow and ice..."*

*The Sage declares that he must go -
"I'll leave you to enjoy the snow!"*

*"Farewell!" the Sage calls. Stars appear -
"I hope you have a happy year..."*

*"What fun!" laughs Rupert. "I can ski!
Hi, everybody! Look at me..."*

"Your turn now!" the Sage tells Mrs. Bear. Rupert's mother reaches deep into the box and pulls out a pair of new winter mittens... "Wonderful!" she laughs. "I'll wear them straightaway." "Time I was getting back to Um Island, now," says the Sage. "The unicorns will be wondering where I've got to!" "Can't you stay for tea and mince pies?" asks Mrs. Bear. "Next year, perhaps," smiles the Sage. "Right now, there's no time to lose. One more spell and I'll be gone..."

"Goodbye, everyone!" calls the Sage as he waves his magic wand in a swirl of stars. "Have a happy new year..." As Rupert looks on, his friend suddenly vanishes - together with the box which has made Nutwood's Christmas so extraordinary... "Never mind!" smiles Mrs. Bear. "At least we've still got lots of snow! You'll be able to try out your new skis." "Good idea!" says Rupert. "Wait until I tell the others where they came from. What a marvellous present..."

THE END

Follow Rupert every day

John Harrold.

in the Daily Express

ANSWERS TO PUZZLES:

(P.90) SPOT THE DIFFERENCE
1) Ticket Collector's punch missing; 2) Girl's shoe strap missing; 3) Feather missing Mrs. Bear's hat; 4) Clasp missing Bill Badger's bag; 5) Buttons missing Bill's waistcoat; 6) Initials missing Rupert's case; 7) Check missing Rupert's scarf; 8) Rupert's spade missing; 9) Pocket missing Mr. Bear's jacket; 10) Sun missing from railway poster.

(P.91) RUPERT'S CROSSWORD
Across:
1. Ransom, 5. Wish, 6. Willie Mouse, 8. Algy Pug, 9. Horace, 11. Podgy, 13. One, 16. Fox Twins, 18. Pearl, 21. Neptune, 24. Squirrel, 27. End, 28. Junk, 29. Edward, 32. Oyster, 34. Out, 37. Bea, 38. China, 40. Tigerlily, 41. Eat, 42. Owl, 43. Escape, 47. Yell, 48. Old, 50. Grow, 51. Open, 53. Stop, 54. Pirate.
Down:
1. Rain, 2. Snow, 3. Bill, 4. Ming, 7. Sage of Um, 9. Horse Chestnut, 10. Gaffer Jarge, 12. Ottoline, 14. Empty, 15. Pink, 17. Ice, 19. June, 20. Chief, 22. Princess, 23. December, 25. Tad, 26. Gregory, 30. Double, 31. Christmas, 33. Rocky Bay, 35. Turtle, 36. Race, 39. Nutwood, 44. Crown, 45. Page, 46. Allow, 49. Last, 52. Pip.

(P.93) WHOSE HAT?

1) Gaffer Jarge, 2) Li-Poo, 3) Cap'n Binnacle, 4) Jack-in-the-box, 5) Castle Guard, 6) Pearl King, 7) Sage of Um, 8) Princess Ottoline, 9) King Neptune, 10) Tad, 11) Autumn Elf, 12) Monkey Guard, 13) Horseman, 14) Chinese Soldier, 15) Chinese Emperor, 16) Bird King.